Codes and
Code Administration

Codes and
Code Administration

**An Introduction to Building Regulations
in the United States**

RICHARD L. SANDERSON

BUILDING OFFICIALS CONFERENCE OF AMERICA, INC.
1313 East 60th Street • Chicago, Illinois 60637

Acknowledgments:

From PUBLIC ADMINISTRATION, by Herbert A. Simon, Donald
W. Smithburg, and Victor A. Thompson. Copyright 1950 by Herbert
A. Simon, Donald W. Smithburg and Victor A. Thompson. Reprinted
by permission of Alfred A. Knopf, Inc.

Rand Corporation Research Study. Copyright (c) 1967 by the Rand
Corporation. Reprinted by permission of the publishers, Little, Brown
and Company (Inc.), and the Rand Corporation.

To

JOSEPH P. WOLFF

With competence and integrity as his only job security, he served as the politically appointed Building Commissioner of the City of Detroit for 28 years.

He became the first Professional Building Official.

Author's Preface

THIS BOOK has been written for use as a textbook by instructors teaching survey courses that include discussions of the use of codes, code enforcement and the administration of building regulations. It is hoped that its contents will also be enlightening and helpful to public administrators, such as mayors and city managers, who have found their code enforcement responsibilities to be extremely perplexing and frustrating. Finally, it has been written to open the eyes of those myopic building officials who have failed to recognize that the real problems of code enforcement are people problems that cannot be solved with trowels, saws or slide rules.

This book is not intended to provide in depth technical details but to lead the reader to the sources of those materials. It is an overview of codes and code enforcement in the United States.

A textbook should, as nearly as possible, be objective. However, since authors are people and people are subjective, it is impossible for them to be completely objective in their writing. This is not a *how to do it book*. It is a *how it is* book laced with editorial comment.

The opinions expressed and statements made in this book are solely those of the author. Some of them are highly controversial and many toes have been stepped on. The author's views do not necessarily reflect nor are they endorsed by The Building Officials Conference of America. The relationship between the author and the organization, insofar as this book is concerned, is purely author-publisher.

For those who might be interested in the educational and experience factors that have led to the author's viewpoints, they range from the College of Engineering at Wayne State University in 1945, to Graduate School (Public Administration) at Illinois Institute of Technology in 1969, and employment during the intervening years as a construction laborer, bricklayer, carpenter, home builder, building inspector, plan examiner, supervisor of building inspectors, head of a municipal building department, Technical Director and currently Executive Director of The Building Officials Conference of America.

Work on this book was started in the fall of 1965, shortly after I joined BOCA as Technical Director, however, the duties that I acquired when I became Executive Director in 1967 brought the project to a halt, except for accumulating and updating reference material, until June of 1969, when the project was resumed. The project would still be dormant except for the time made available to me because of the competence and dedication of BOCA Technical Director, Gaylon R. Claiborne.

For reference materials, I have drawn heavily on the publications of the various federal agencies, the records of The Building Officials Conference of America and the textbooks from my courses in public administration.

For the opportunities that have allowed me to pursue the fulfilling career that has led to the writing of this book, I am indebted to Joseph P. Wolff to whom the book is dedicated and to my wife, Agnes, whose tolerant understanding and encouragement has given me the freedom to study, moonlight and politic; and whose feminine charm has opened many doors for me that no male could open alone.

Manuscripts do not just suddenly appear in a form that is acceptable to the printer and this one was no exception. The ability of my secretary, Joan Fox, to interpret the hieroglyphics that I substitute for handwriting and convert them to beautifully typewritten pages is absolutely amazing. For that ability and her always helpful and cheerful spirit, I am especially grateful.

R.L.S.

CHICAGO, ILLINOIS
JULY 12, 1969

Contents

Introduction

FOR over half a century the subject of building codes and code enforcement in the United States has been controversial, yet in all that time no one has ever written a textbook on the subject. Architects and engineers are graduated from our universities with no more knowledge of the subject than an awareness that there are *codes* enforced by local governments that might affect their design concepts.

Local government officials have suffered under an illusion that prior training in architecture, engineering or a building trade was *in itself* ample qualification for a position in code enforcement.

This book is an attempt to fill a void in the literature of construction in the United States. It is an attempt to place between the front and back covers of one small book, the *big picture* of codes and code enforcement.

Once the decision was made to write the book, the problem then became two-fold. First, what should be included? and Second, How should the material be arranged?

The author decided that although intertwined, there are actually two subjects that must be covered; the codes themselves and code enforcement or, more appropriately, the administration of building regulations.

Since there are two subjects, the book is divided into two parts. Part I, Codes, covers the development and influences on codes from Hammurabi to HUD. While Chapter I is a capsule history of the codes in use in the United States right up to today, the basis for the requirements contained in the codes is found in Chapter II. The use of nationally recognized standards as an essential part of the concept of *performance* building codes is covered in detail in Chapter III and some of the present-day influences that effect code requirements both locally and on a nation-wide basis are examined in Chapter IV. The contribution of the model codes as the basis of the code system in the

1

United States is established in Chapter V which leads to a lengthy discussion of the question: Is a Federal Building Code Necessary? in Chapter VI.

Chapter VII explains the role played by the Department of Housing and Urban Development and other federal agencies in the broad field of building regulations. Finally, the Building Officials' Organizations are examined in Chapter VIII as *professional societies* from the standpoint of building officials and *trade associations* from the standpoint of industry.

Part II, Administration, covers the broad spectrum of problems encountered in this highly specialized and little understood function of government.

In Chapter IX code enforcement is identified as a highly specialized area of law enforcement and the building official as a law enforcement officer. Chapter X spells out the role of the chief executive and legislature in code enforcement and emphasizes the importance of the chief executive *acting like one.*

Chapter XI is devoted to an examination of the scope of activities of a code enforcement agency and the need for consolidating all code enforcement activities into one department. Chapter XII is directed towards dispelling the *myths* about the qualifications needed by code enforcement officers and outlining the qualifications that *are* important.

The content of chapters XIII, XIV and XV could have been included under the one heading of *code enforcement,* however, it was necessary to break the subject matter down into office operations, field inspections and code enforcement so that examples could be used to show all of the facets that comprise the totality of code enforcement.

In Chapter XVI the code enforcement professional is identified: how and why some make it while others with similar backgrounds do not. And finally, six steps are outlined for developing the corps of professional code enforcement officers that are needed to police the development, rebuilding and maintenance of our country.

PART ONE

Codes

Historical Development

M AN'S concern for the safety of his buildings has been recorded in the laws of some of the most ancient civilizations. The death penalty was often imposed on the builder of a faulty building.

King Hammurabi, in approximately 1700 B.C., attempted to codify the many laws of the lands he had conquered. Article 229 of that code reads as follows: "If a builder has built a house for a man, and his work is not strong, and if the house he has built falls in and kills the householder, that builder shall be slain."[1]

The Polynesians required that a live slave be placed under each corner post to insure that the building was properly supported.

The harsh penalties and inhuman requirements of these early regulations were the forerunners of the many detailed codes and ordinances that are necessary to the protection of the public health, safety, and welfare in our modern society.

The collapse of a wooden amphitheatre near Rome, which killed or injured 50,000 people in 27 A.D., moved the Senate to make new regulations for the safety of public places of entertainment; however, the designer of the collapsed structure was merely banished from Rome and from Italy.[2]

Fire hazards inherent in buildings were the basis of the earliest building regulations in England and the United States.

---

[1] *Ancient Rome,* cited by R. C. Colling and Hal Colling (eds.), *Modern Building Inspection* (Los Angeles: Building Standards Monthly Publishing Company, 1950), p. 12.

[2] *Ibid.,* p. 13.

A pioneer building code was promulgated by the Lord Mayor of London, Henry Fitz-Elwyne, in 1189. Known as the Assize of Buildings, this now famous document set forth the method approved for the building of party walls, and regulated their use in a manner that placed high value on strong stone walls which acted as fire stops.[3]

Apparently, there was little or no enforcement of Henry Fitz-Elwyne's code, however, since investigations of the great fire of 1666 revealed that 300,000 souls were jammed into the half-mile wide and mile long city which was enclosed in 35 foot high masonry walls. Sixteen thousand houses, most of them two stories, were butted against each other and frequently without the masonry fire walls required by the city's building code.

The fire consumed all major public buildings, a thousand taverns, eighty-seven churches, and over thirteen thousand homes. Miraculously only six persons were known to have died in the flames.

Conditions were so bad in the city before the fire that English monarchs had not resided there regularly for six centuries. Nobles and rich merchants had also abandoned the city for the peace and quiet of the suburbs.[4]

A fire in 1630 burned down a house in Boston and sparks from it ignited that of a neighbor so that it, too, burned down. Thereupon, in the words of the Governor, "We have ordered that no man shall build his chimney with wood, nor cover his house with thatch, which was readily assented to."

The contrast between the colonial village of 1630 and the industrial city of three centuries later is suggestive of the contrast between the first building regulations and the requirements of today. The development of tall buildings housing many people offers not only fire hazards but innumerable other safety problems, and it is necessary that there be regulations to assure, as far as humanly possible, public safety. The application of technical and scientific progress has made possible the growth of modern cities with their skyscrapers and large factories, but the same technical and scientific knowledge, if erroneously or incompetently applied, creates dangers to life and property vastly more serious than the loss of several thatched cottages in Colonial Boston.

---

[3] Edna Trull, *Administration of Regulatory Inspectional Services in American Cities* (New York: Municipal Administration Service, 1932), p. 81.
[4] Arthur Veysey, "The Great London Fire," *Chicago Tribune Sunday Magazine*, March 5, 1967, pp. 68-71.

6

Any considerable concentration of population, in fact, should protect itself from unnecessary fire hazards and other building defects, as well as from the shoddy construction work of speculative builders, by the establishment and enforcement of adequate building standards. A small city may suffer as disastrously, in proportion to its size, as a large city from devastating fires, and jerry-built houses constitute not only a menace to health and safety, but a serious economic loss to the community. Values created by the prolongation of the life of a city's structural improvements for a single year through scientific building regulations will thoroughly justify the expense entailed.[5]

Permits for chimneys were often issued by fire departments and the only part of a building that was inspected was the chimney.

The first building law on record in the United States was passed in the Dutch city of New Amsterdam in 1625 and consisted of rules as to types, locations and roof coverings of houses. Since the population of the city was not over 200 at this time, the need for a fundamental building code had not become apparent.[6]

Major disasters in places of public assembly and institutional buildings such as hospitals and homes for the aged gave rise to a public demand for rigid regulations.

The exact tragedy that resulted in the enactment of the first law for the inspection of existing places of public assembly is not known, but a regulation passed in New Orleans in 1856 stated that: "The Mayor and Surveyor shall examine theatres and places of public resort for structural stability, and to take suitable measures to prevent accidents that might result from any negligence in the construction of the building or from any mismanagement of the proprietors."[7]

Severe losses by fire insurance companies prompted the National Board of Fire Underwriters (now the American Insurance Association) in 1905 to publish the Recommended National Building Code to guide municipalities concerned with reducing the fire hazards in and about buildings.

---

[5] Trull.

[6] R. C. Colling and Hal Colling (eds.), *Modern Building Inspection* (Los Angeles: Building Standards Monthly Publishing Company, 1950), p. 48.

[7] *Ibid*, p. 56.

Because the Board desired to provide a code that was suitable for enactment into law, structural safety regulations as well as those pertaining directly to fire protection were included. Many cities have used this code as the basis for their own codes or have adopted it in its entirety by reference.

Fire and casualty insurance companies carry on this activity because that which serves the public interest in these matters also serves their interest.

The Code has been drafted by engineers of the American Insurance Association with help and assistance from many sources. Approved USA Standards and nationally recognized standards of trade associations have been widely used in the Code.

Provisions for safety to life require exit ways that will be safe to use under fire conditions and also require physical restrictions to the spread of fire such as: limitation of areas; proper enclosure of all vertical openings, shafts, and elevators; fire walls (and in some cases exterior walls) have stability under fire conditions as well as fire resistance; restrictions on flame spread of materials used as interior finish; protection of window openings against fire exposure; and installation of automatic sprinkler systems for certain occupancies, including those with readily combustible contents.

Lack of one or more of the above features has frequently been an important factor in the injury or death of persons from fires in buildings. The requirements of the National Building Code take into account the accumulation of years of study of these factors by men familiar with the phenomena of fires and their spread in buildings.

The National Building Code contains the latest nationally recognized working stresses for basic building materials including aluminum, light gage cold-formed steel, prestressed concrete, and reinforced masonry. It allows the selected use of plastics in building construction.

The Code provides for new architectural concepts such as roofed-over malls, steep-sloped roofs, and dome-shaped structures.

Buildings of unlimited area are covered by stipulating the conditions under which such buildings are permitted.

High hazard occupancies are covered by requiring compliance with nationally recognized good practice where such exists and giving certain requirements for other high hazard occupancies.[8]

---

[8]American Insurance Association, Engineering and Safety Department, *Building Codes—The National Building Code of the American Insurance Association* (March, 1967), p. 1.

The Recommended National Building Code was the only nationally recognized *model* building code until 1927 when the first model code, prepared by building officials, The Uniform Building Code, was published by the Pacific Coast Building Officials Conference (now the International Conference of Building Officials). This code is used extensively on the West coast and has been adopted by some cities east of the Rocky Mountains.

The Uniform Building Code is maintained as a "living" document and is kept up-to-date to hold pace with new developments in the construction industry. A complete new edition of the Code is published every three years for the use of the members. Publications include seven volumes of the Uniform Building Code and the Book of Standards. These volumes include the basic Uniform Building Code, the Mechanical Code, the Housing Code, a Sign Code, a Dangerous Building Code, a Dwelling House Construction pamphlet and the Short Form of the Uniform Building Code.[9]

The unique problems affecting construction in the South prompted the building officials in that area to prepare a model code and in 1945, the Southern Standard Building Code was published by the Southern Building Code Congress. This is the predominant building code in the Southern States and the Plumbing, Gas and Housing Codes published by SBCC have also gained wide acceptance in that area.

The Building Officials Conference of America, established in 1915 as a professional society of building officials, first published its Basic Building Code in 1950. It is now the most widely used code in the Northeast and Midwest. BOCA also publishes a Basic Housing Code, Basic Fire Prevention Code and a Basic Plumbing Code.

Despite the extensive adoption of the *model* codes, the major cities of the nation, with a few notable exceptions (Detroit, St. Louis, and Memphis have adopted the Basic Building Code), seem determined to go their own way. After several years of development and expenditure of one-and-a-half million dollars, New York City adopted a new building code in 1968 and

---

[9] International Conference of Building Officials, *International Conference of Building Officials: Its Operating Structure and Service Facilities* (Pasadena: International Conference of Building Officials, 1964.)

9

acknowledged that it was patterned after the Basic Building Code. In 1969, Philadelphia completed and adopted a new code based essentially on the requirements of the Basic Building Code.

State Codes

Code enforcement has traditionally been a function of local government in the United States. However, a few states have enacted or provided in some manner for the establishment of state-wide building codes. In no case, however, is there an all-inclusive code that is mandatory throughout the entire state for all construction. State building codes are in three major forms, none of which is used in more than a half dozen states. The forms are: model codes that may be adopted by the political subdivisions of the state; mandatory codes that exclude buildings to be used for certain occupancies (such as one- and two-family dwellings) ; and codes that apply only to the construction of state owned buildings, or those that are financed with public funds.

California, Indiana, North Carolina, Ohio, and Wisconsin are the only states that have mandatory state-wide building codes, and in no case, are they applicable to all construction within the state. The Indiana, North Carolina, and Wisconsin codes do not apply to one- and two-family dwellings, and Ohio exempts dwellings containing up to three dwelling units. Farm buildings are excluded by all of the state codes and in California, the state code applies to dwellings but excludes public buildings and places of employment.

Except for North Carolina, the mandatory state codes are minimum regulations which apply to all construction within the scope of their authority. They do not supersede local codes however, that are equal to or more stringent and otherwise not in conflict with the state code. Local governments in North Carolina can only adopt local building regulations on approval of the State Building Code Council. It is the policy of the council to approve only minor revisions to the state code.

Maryland, Nevada, Minnesota, New Hampshire, and Idaho have adopted mandatory building codes for state owned or state financed projects.

Connecticut, New Jersey, and New York have assigned state agencies the responsibility of developing model building codes for voluntary adoption by local governments. Minnesota will make its building code for public buildings available to its political subdivisions for adoption by reference.

New York has a model state code which may be adopted by local governments by a simple resolution; however, once adopted, it cannot be changed except by special petitions to the State Building Codes Council.[10] This *no change* provision quite effectively prevents the adoption by local governments of standards higher than those in the state code.

The significance of the *no change* provision bears emphasis, because it is the antithesis of the code philosophy of all other states that state code requirements are *minimums*. In New York State, they are also *maximums*.

[10] James R. Brown, Rita C. Griswald, and Dale M. Sharkey, *A Study Concerning the Need for Uniform Building Code for the Capitol Region,* Prepared for the Land Use and Housing Committee of the Regional Advisory Committee by the Regional Affairs Center, University of Hartford (Hartford: Regional Affairs Center, 1967), pp. 18-23.

The Basis For Code
Requirements

I N the preceding chapter, we have established that building codes were developed over the years as a part of man's effort to prevent those disasters that are within his power to prevent. We have also established that governments, both ancient and modern, have recognized that they have a responsibility to protect their people by enacting and enforcing building regulations. In this chapter we will examine the nature of a building code and the basis for code requirements.

What Is a Building Code?

A building code is a legal document which sets forth requirements to protect the public health, safety and general welfare as they relate to the construction and occupancy of buildings and structures. This is accomplished by establishing the minimum acceptable conditions for matters found to be in need of regulation. Topics generally covered are exits, fire protection, structural design, sanitary facilities, light and ventilation, etc.[1]

Rudolph P. Miller, who founded the Building Officials Conference of America in 1915, stated the purposes of a building code as follows:

The building laws should provide only for such requirements with

---

[1] George N. Thompson, *Preparation and Revision of Building Codes*, U. S. Department of Commerce, National Bureau of Standards, Building Materials and Structures Report BMS 116 (Washington: U. S. Government Printing Office, 1949), p. 2.

respect to building construction and closely related matters, as are absolutely necessary for the protection of persons who have no voice in the manner of construction or the arrangement of buildings with which they involuntarily come in contact. Thus, when buildings are comparatively small, are far apart, and their use is limited to the owners and builders of them, so that, in case of failure of any kind they are not a source of danger to others, no necessity for building restrictions would exist. But as these buildings are placed closer to one another or on the line of a neighbor's property, or as they are used first as a matter of necessity and later as a regular practice growing out of necessity, by persons other than the owners, as in the case of guests at hotels, customers in business buildings, workers in factories, tenants in multiple buildings, etc., then increasingly greater requirements are needed to secure for the occupants and their neighbors, structural safety, security against fire, sufficiency of light and air to preserve health, etc.[2]

The typical building code regulates the construction, alterations, maintenance, repair and demolition of buildings and structures. It may or may not regulate the installation and maintenance of mechanical systems and equipment within or appurtenant to buildings and structures. Many experts look upon the entire complex of regulatory codes, including electrical, plumbing, heating, boilers, pressure vessels, air pollution, air conditioning, refrigeration, elevators, and flammable liquids as integral parts of the comprehensive building code. Those holding this view use the term, "big 'B' building code", to indicate that it is all-encompassing.

Housing codes are basically maintenance codes which also regulate the environmental factors of residential buildings and, in the case of rental property, the facilities that must be supplied by the landlord. Housing codes are frequently a chapter in the building codes of major cities, but there is a trend today to separate the housing code from the building code.

Laymen frequently confuse zoning ordinances and subdivision requirements with the building code. The confusion arises because the zoning ordinance is usually enforced by the same agency that enforces the building code. Subdivision regulations,

---

[2] Paul E. Baseler, "Basic Principles of Building Codes," *Local Building Regulations,* ed. Paul E. Baseler, (Chicago: Building Officials Conference of America, Inc., 1963).

although generally not enforced by the code enforcement agency, do have a direct effect on the ultimate cost of buildings and, therefore, are mistakenly placed in the same category as codes.

The scope of the requirements in the big "B" building code reflect its broad objectives.

Types of Codes

Building codes are commonly classified as being *specification codes* or *performance codes*. The *specification code* describes in detail exactly what materials are to be used, the size and spacing of units, and the methods of assembly.

The *performance code*, on the other hand, prescribes the objective to be accomplished and allows broad leeway to the designers in selecting the materials and methods that will achieve the required results.

As a practical matter, a pure *performance code* would be impossible to enforce because the only proof of inadequate design or poor construction would be the failure of the building. What is important about a *performance code* is that where specifications are used, provisions are made for the substitution of alternate systems and materials that can be proved adequate by tests or engineering calculations.

All four model building codes used in the United States today are considered by the publishing organizations to be *performance codes*. Actually, they are all a judicious combination of standard specifications and performance requirements. Although these codes establish performance requirements that the designers must accomplish, the quality of the materials selected and the manner in which they are used is governed by material standards and accepted engineering design criteria, which are specification documents. The proof of performance of the methods and materials selected by the designer is governed by nationally recognized and accepted test standards.

The Requirements

Although the bases for modern code requirements are a mystery to the laymen and to many building officials, most of them are based on the natural scientific laws, known properties of materials and the inherent hazards of uses or occupancies.

Adequate records have been kept of fires, building failures, panics and natural disasters such as earthquakes, hurricanes and floods to establish minimum criteria for the design of buildings.

It is a combination of the natural scientific laws and the compiled and evaluated statistics of disasters that form the basis for code requirements.

Since the first building regulations in the United States were enacted because of disastrous fires and the first model building code was published by the National Board of Fire Underwriters, it is not surprising that building codes devote considerable attention to fire safety requirements. For example, all of the model building codes provide for the establishment of fire limits within which only buildings of certain types of construction may be erected. The object of establishing fire limits is to restrict the spread of fire to limited areas within a city.

Another fire safety requirement is the limitation of the maximum heights and areas of buildings depending on the type of construction and occupancy.

The prime purpose of limiting the heights and areas of building is to equalize the fire risk to a community for all use groups and all types of construction. For example, the height and area limitation table in the Basic Building Code is based on two factors: the "U" factor which expresses the inherent fire hazard of a building's use or occupancy; and the "C" factor which represents the actual fire resistance of the type of the building's construction as determined by standard fire tests.

The use factor "U" was determined by a study of the fire experience record reported in the N.F.P.A. (National Fire Protection Association) Quarterly for twelve representative states over the period of 1930 to 1952. The analysis was based on the number of fires in each use group, the number of lives lost per fire and the amount of property damage per fire, all expressed in percentages of the total amounts for all use groups. These were combined to establish the relative hazards of the several occupancy groups. The inverse of these quantities represents the relative degree of fire safety, as the hazard varies inversely to that quantity. In the determination of the "U" factor, there is no consideration given to the type of construction.

To provide for the effect of construction type on the relative fire safety of buildings, the factor "C" was developed assigning the value of unity of the most hazardous construction type—the unprotected wood frame, type 4C.[3]

In spite of the fact that considerable research and effort have gone into the establishment of the height and area limitations found in building codes, there is still no nationally recognized standard for determining allowable heights and areas. As this book goes to press an ad hoc committee comprised of representatives of all model code groups, design professionals, the National Fire Protection Association, major trade associations, and interested federal agencies, is trying to develop the badly needed standard. Committees are also working on the same problem in Europe and Australia.

Occupancy or use classifications are established according to the inherent hazards of the use. The number of people, the conditions of occupancy or confined spaces, the amounts and kinds of materials and the equipment utilized are all factors that must be considered. Uses having similar characteristics are grouped together to minimize the number of classifications that must be considered.

The safety provided by the several typical construction methods can be used to offset the hazards of the various use groups. These are, therefore, grouped into *types of construction* according to their proven capacity to resist fire. There are four basic types of construction although they are usually subdivided further in most building codes. The construction types range from those having a high fire resistance potential to those having a high susceptibility to fire.

To further distinguish the types of construction, two major characteristics are considered. These characteristics are the combustibility or noncombustibility of permitted materials. Those types of construction wherein noncombustible materials are required so that the elements of the structure will not contribute fuel to the fire are classified as *noncombustible*. Those types in which combustible materials are permitted and which *will* contribute fuel to the fire, are classified *combustible*.

Further breakdowns are established by the degree of fire protection provided and the fire resistance of material used to protect the structural elements of the buildings.

---

[3] Joseph E. Bartell, "Analysis of the BOCA Codes," *ibid.*

17

Some of the other fire safety requirements commonly found in building codes are proper enclosure of vertical openings, shafts and elevators; restrictions on the potential flame spread of materials used for interior finish; protection of window openings from exposure to fire; and automatic sprinkler systems for occupancies having readily combustible contents.

Many building uses involve special hazards which require extra protection in addition to the normal requirements of their general use group classification. These special uses are usually regulated by nationally recognized safety standards that are an integral part of the model building codes or recognized as accepted engineering practice.

Safety to Life

The most important life safety requirements in a building code are those covering building exits. Like the height and area requirements, the determination of safe exit requirements is based on research and observation of past conditions and experiences. It is far from an exact science. There is a nationally recognized standard available however, which is based on the best judgement of men well qualified in this field. This standard is published by the National Fire Protection Association as the Safety to Life Code. Known as the Building Exits Code until 1967, it is the reference document behind the exit requirements of most building codes in the United States.

The theory from which exit requirements have been developed is that every person in a building, in a minimum amount of time, should be able to reach an area within the building that has been constructed to provide a predetermined degree of protection from fire; and once within that area, should be able to reach the outside of the building through a continuous passage, safely protected from the hazards of smoke and fire.

The number of exits required, their size and location is dependent, to a large extent, upon the use or occupancy of the building.

In buildings containing occupancies that require a number of small or moderately sized rooms arranged along a common corridor, as in a school or office building, the exitway is considered to begin at the point of discharge to the outside. At grade

18

level, this could be an exit door directly outside or a *Grade Passageway* designed specifically to provide safe travel to the outside. On upper floors, the exitway begins where one passes from the corridor, through a fire door, into an enclosed stairway that provides safe travel to the outside.

In the case of rooms or buildings used for public assembly, the doors from assembly rooms to the outside *or* to an enclosed corridor are the exits. When assembly room exit doors discharge into a corridor or passageway, the corridor or passageway becomes part of the room's exit facilities. Assembly rooms having a maximum capacity of less than one hundred (100) persons are generally not considered places of public assembly for exit requirement purposes.

The structural design requirements in building codes are based on nationally recognized standards developed and maintained by accredited, authoritative agencies in the fields involved. These standards are, in fact, the detailed specifications that make the *performance code* concept feasible. While the building code does not specify *what* materials and/or methods must be used, the standards do specify *how* they are to be used once they are selected.

Information available only from agencies of the federal government is utilized in building codes. The Seismic Probability Map of the United States, developed by the U.S. Coast and Geodetic Survey, and the wind velocity maps of the United States Weather Bureau are made an integral part of model building code design requirements.

Environmental Requirements

In Chapter I we mentioned the environmental requirements as being part of the *housing code,* however, the same or similar requirements are also found in building codes and with good reason. A code enforcement agency cannot justify issuing a building permit that would allow construction of a building that would be in violation of the *housing code*.

Requirements covering natural and artificial light and ventilation, room sizes, ceiling heights and sanitary facilities are generally found in building codes.

In this chapter we have explained what a building code is

and the basis for code requirements. We have also established that many of the requirements are based on experience rather than scientific facts. We mentioned that recognized authoritative agencies develop and publish standards for use of materials and methods.

20

III

The Use of Standards in Codes

I N the last chapter, we discussed the nature of building codes and the basis for code requirements. We determined that many code requirements are based on experience rather than scientific facts. We also pointed out that many building code provisions are nationally recognized standards developed by authoritative agencies in various fields. In this chapter we will identify the standards writing and publishing organizations, their nature and methods of operation. We shall also examine some of the methods used to incorporate the standards into the requirements of building codes.

Standards Issuing Agencies

Many agencies develop and publish standards. Trade associations, engineering societies and other professional organizations prepare standards that are widely accepted and recognized as authoritative in their particular field of competence. Four standards issuing agencies deserve special attention since the standards they issue constitute the bulk of those used in building codes. These agencies are:

The American Society for Testing and Materials
The National Fire Protection Association
American National Standards Institute, Inc.
The United States Department of Commerce

American Society for Testing and Materials (A.S.T.M.)

The American Society for Testing and Materials develops

and publishes standard specifications for materials and standard methods of testing materials or assemblies. The Society operates through a system of technical committees, which are organized under the rules of the Society, but are autonomous to a large degree. Each group establishes its own by-laws and governs its own operations with the assistance and guidance, but not the direction, of the Society staff. Standards may be approved and issued as *tentative* and used for several years before sufficient experience is gained to warrant identification as a standard without the *tentative* designation.

Technical committees are required to review *tentative* standards periodically to determine if they should be approved as a *standard*.

The American Society for Testing and Materials publishes all of its standards applicable to building codes in one volume under the title ASTM Standards in Building Codes. This valuable publication is amended annually and a new edition issued.

National Fire Protection Association (N.F.P.A.)

The National Fire Protection Association develops and publishes fire protection, fire prevention and fire safety standards. The Association operates through a committee system similar to that used by the American Society for Testing and Materials, however, the technical committees are controlled as to membership and procedures by the Association. The technical committees of NFPA may initiate standards or review standards developed by other organizations, such as ASTM. Recommendations for adoption or modification are made in accordance with the best judgement of the committee members.

Once adopted, an NFPA standard may be published under an NFPA identification number without reference to the originating agency. There is usually a cross reference, however. All NFPA standards are published in a ten volume set called the National Fire Codes. Some NFPA standards are also processed and identified as ANSI standards by the American National Standards Institute.

American National Standards Institute, Inc. (A.N.S.I.)

The American National Standards Institute serves as a coordinating agency for the approval of standards produced by other recognized authoritative agencies and encourages the development of standards through an established procedure that requires broad representation on technical committees and review of technical committee recommendations by a *Standards Board* prior to final approval and issuance as an ANSI standard.

ANSI has two methods for establishing standards. The method used for approval of standards produced by other agencies is called the *existing standards* method and the one utilizing technical committees is called the *sectional committee* method. In either case, the standards are not formulated by ANSI.

When the *existing standards* method is used, ANSI adopts a standard that has already been produced by another agency and assigns it an ANSI identification number which designates it as an American National Standard.

When the *sectional committee* method is used, ANSI acts as a correlating agency to determine the following:

a. If there is a need for a requested standard.

b. If there is an existing representative activity for developing the requested standard.

If the first question is answered in the affirmative and the second in the negative, ANSI encourages the forming of a *sectional committee* of representative organizations and/or agencies considered to have a legitimate interest in the subject matter of the proposed standard.

A conference may be called by ANSI of all organizations, agencies, companies or individuals that may be even remotely concerned with a proposed standard. When such a conference determines that there is need for the development of a standard, the sponsors organize the *sectional committee* with assistance as required from the ANSI staff. The *sectional committee* then becomes an autonomous group, (subject to ANSI rules and procedures) and develops the needed standard.

ANSI approval of a standard is dependent upon meeting an explicit set of conditions that result in a determination that a *consensus* of opinion exists for acceptance of a proposed standard.

If there are dissenting opinions or negative votes by members of a sectional committee, the reasons for them are carefully *weighed*. If objections are found to be based on the general public interest, the standard may not be approved. If they are found to be the result of personal or preferential consideration, they may be disregarded. Approval of proposed standards for publication as ANSI standards is dependent upon a review of the make-up and findings of the *sectional committee* by a *Standards Board* of carefully selected representatives from the field involved. Building materials and construction standards are within the purview of the *Construction Standards Board*.[1]

United States Department of Commerce (U.S.D.C.)

The United States Department of Commerce has participated in the development of voluntary standards for products, processes and materials as an essential public service since 1901. Standards developed and published by USDC cover terms, classes, sizes, dimensions, capacities, quality levels, performance, criteria, testing equipment, and test procedures.

The Department engages in this activity in recognition of the importance, the advantages, and the benefits of standardization activities and by authority of a March 3, 1901 Act of Congress; as amended July 22 ,1950.

The Department participates in the development of voluntary standards when the standard is deemed appropriate by meeting the following criteria:

    a. It is not contrary to the public interest,

    b. It has national effect or implication,

    c. It has apparent industry-wide interest or endorsement, and

    d. It is not such that it can be processed according to needs or desires of the industry by a nationally recognized private standardizing body.

The *product standards* published by USDC are the end product of a joint venture between industry and government. The roles of

---

[1] John J. Uicker, "The Use of Standards in Building Codes", *Local Building Regulations,* ed. Paul E. Baseler (Chicago: Building Officials Conference of America, Inc., 1963) .

24

each are spelled out in USDC Department Order No. 90, revised January 30, 1964.

It is the role of the Department, in responding to a specific request from industry, to assist in the establishment of a voluntary standard by:

a. Initiating and participating in the development of the standard.
b. Supplying such assistance and review as is necessary to assure the technical soundness of the standard.
c. Seeing that the standard is representative of the views of producers, distributors, users, and consumers.
d. Seeking satisfactory adjustment of valid points of disagreement.
e. Publishing the standards.
f. Establishing a hallmark which may be used on or for products that meet the requirements set forth in the standard.

It is the role of industry to contribute to the development of a voluntary standard by:

a. Initiating and participating in the development of a standard.
b. Providing technical counsel on a standard.
c. Promoting the use of, and support for, the standard.

Initiating and Developing Product Standards

Any group of manufacturers, distributors, consumers, users, or testing laboratories, or any State or Federal agency concerned with a particular product, may request the Department to participate in the development and publication of a voluntary standard for that product under the following procedures:

A written request containing the following information must be submitted to the Department:

a. The purpose and scope of a suggested standard.
b. A succinct statement of the need for the suggested standard and why it is desirable that the standard be developed through the Department of Commerce procedures.
c. A statement of reasons why the suggested standard would be in the public interest.

d. Available technical data essential to the suggested standard and its further development, such as physical, mechanical, chemical or performance requirements, and production figures for the common stock varieties.

e. Any other information which may be necessary as a basis for a discussion by others.

f. The names and addresses of the members of the group making the request if it is not a nationally recognized group.

When a proposed standard has been accepted for development by the Department, it is subjected to an impartial technical review by an appropriate individual or agency. The reviewing individual or agency may be government or nongovernment, but not associated with the proponent of the standard.

The proposed standard is then made available for public comment and is circulated by the Department to appropriate producers, distributors, users, consumers, and other interested groups for consideration and comments.

Comments and suggestions received by the Department as a result of circulation of the proposed standard are then considered by the proponent or technical committee. Adjustments to the original proposal that are technically sound and will secure the greatest acceptance of the standard by the industry will then be recommended.

Adjusted proposed standards are submitted to a Standard Review Committee for approval and recommendation to the Department for acceptance. Once the Department is satisfied that all criteria and procedures have been met and there is no legal objection to the recommended standard, appropriate public notice is given and the recommended standard is distributed for acceptance.

Before a product standard is printed, the Department appoints a Standing Committee to receive and consider proposals to revise or amend the standard in light of changing circumstances and to make appropriate recommendations to the Department.

Voluntary Standards Are Not Mandatory

Standards published by USDC are voluntary standards and

by themselves have no mandatory or legally binding effect. One may choose to use or not to use such a standard.

The initial costs of publishing voluntary standards are borne by the sponsoring group, which receives 1,000 copies. Additional copies are sold by the Public Printer in accordance with the government printing laws and regulations.

References to standards published by USDC may be made in contracts, codes, advertising, invoices, announcements, product labels, etc., within the policies established by the Department.

The Department requires that standards be revised whenever any of their basic or substantive provisions are determined to be inadequate.

USDC standards may be withdrawn by the Department at any time upon reasonable public notice if a standard is obsolete, technically inadequate, no longer acceptable to and used by industry, contrary to law, not in the public interest, or for other reasons, and revision is not feasible or would serve no useful purpose.[2]

Industry Standards

In addition to the four major standards publishing agencies, certain industry groups publish their own standards. There is a trend at this time to process all of these through the American National Standards Institute. If the organizations publishing model building codes are successful in their efforts to promote publication by ANSI of all standards used in the codes in one volume or set, this would seem inevitable.

Methods of Utilizing Standards in Codes

The most widely accepted method of utilizing standards as an integral part of code requirements is to reference them in the appendix of the code and then spell out the conditions of their applicability in the text of the code. Some codes include standards in the text or compile and publish them in a separate volume. There is a movement away from the latter method since the standards are constantly being revised and it is easier and less

---

[2]*Federal Register*, December 10, 1965, cited in *BOCA NEWS*, XIV, (February 1966), pp. 6-8.

expensive to change references in an appendix than to reprint entire codes or volumes of codes.

Classification of Standards

There are three basic classifications of standards used in building codes. They are:

1. Engineering Practice Standards
2. Material Standards
3. Test Standards (three types)
   a. structural unit tests
   b. durability tests
   c. fire tests

Engineering Practice Standards generally define methods of design, fabrication, or construction and specify accepted design procedure, engineering formulae and calculation methods as well as good practice standards. These standards are specifications formulated by special interests in the construction industry and are often an expression of optimum conditions rather than the minimums for safe practice. Only those portions of standards spelling out safety limits should be considered mandatory requirements. *Those elements of standards exceeding safety requirements should be regarded as acceptable but not required by the building code.*

Material standards are specifications establishing quality requirements and physical properties of materials or manufactured products. Those portions of such standards that are concerned with safety should be considered mandatory; *those portions that exceed requirements for safety should merely be considered as acceptable.*

Test standards should always be considered mandatory since it is impossible to measure performance without using standard methods.

The Voluntary Standards System

It should be apparent from the preceding descriptions of the standards publishing agencies and their operations that standards are developed in the United States as they are needed, by the interest groups that are most vitally affected by them, but with the advice and consent of other interested parties. They are processed and published by private organizations insofar as practical, but by the Federal Government when necessary or more appropriate.

An understanding of the standards system in the United States and the use of standards in codes, places the cumulative scientific, engineering and industrial know-how of America at the fingertips of the Building Official. He may accept with confidence, the materials, systems and practices that meet the nationally recognized standards.

Standards and Codes

Confusion on the part of some local governments unfamiliar with standards activities has resulted in the adoption of some standards as local ordinances. This problem was created, in part, by the practice of some standards producing agencies in designating their standards as "Building Code Requirements for...".

Attempts were made by some organizations to develop building code requirements for their own individual segment of the construction industry. Each industry taking this approach inserted requirements that were not related to safety but were designed to uphold the voluntary standards of the industry. In addition, since each of the *Codes* was developed by separate committees, overlapping and language difficulties were encountered, especially in regard to administration. The conflicting interests of the several branches of the construction industry insofar as fire protection and general requirements were concerned proved this system thoroughly impractical.

The impracticality of securing local adoption of a myriad of special interest *Codes* has resulted in strong support by industry for the model building codes.

There are 417 standards listed in the 1965 Edition of the Basic Building Code published by the Building Officials Conference of America. The impracticality of explaining the content of each of those standards to a city council is self-evident.[3]

In this chapter we have examined the nature and operations of the major standards publishing agencies, the development of standards and their use in building codes.

---

[3] Uicker.

Influences on Code Requirements

I N Chapter III, we explained the standards development process in the United States and the use of standards as building code requirements. In this chapter we will look at the role of the industry associations and other groups that play an important part in developing and revising the substantive provisions of building codes.

Many forces influence the development and revision of building regulations (code requirements). These forces of influence are exerted by groups or organizations affected by the regulations, but not necessarily the group being regulated. The degree of influence of one group may adversely affect the welfare of another and it is necessary to exercise constant knowledgeable vigilance to protect the best interest of the general public.

The prime influence groups until recently have been in the private sector.[1] They are trade associations, lending institutions, insurance underwriters, manufacturers, professional societies, educational institutions, churches, labor unions, contractors associations and property owners associations. A vociferous individual with a cause is sometimes responsible for generating public support for his position to the point where legislative action is taken and code requirements are written or revised. The success of Ralph Nader in influencing automobile safety legislation is a good example of how effective one individual can be when he dedicates himself to a cause. For the most part it is the recognized

---

[1] The role of the Department of Housing and Urban Development and other Federal agencies will be discussed in detail in Chapter VII.

formal organizations that have the greatest impact on code requirements.

Accredited Authoritative Agencies

Those organizations having a direct and continuing interest in code requirements employ professional staffs to work directly with the model code publishing groups and with federal, state and local government agencies promulgating and enforcing building regulations. There are one hundred forty Accredited Authoritative Agencies listed in the Appendix of the 1965 Edition of the Basic Building Code.[2]

These groups exert their influence directly, or indirectly, through the model code publishing organizations on the secondary or public sector groups, which are government agencies at all levels; federal, state, county and municipal.

The motivations of the primary influence groups are as diverse as their organizational purposes. The effect of their influence, however, is not necessarily in proportion to the apparent importance of the group to a legislative body.

A local Electrical Code that requires the use of metal conduit for wiring in the construction of dwelling houses and adds $150.00 to $300.00 to the cost of a house, when the National Electrical Code[3] permits the use of Romex (nonmetallic sheathed cable), does not benefit the house owner, who in his role as a voter, would appear to be of considerable importance to the local legislative body.

The enforcement of building regulations (codes) in the United States has traditionally and properly been a function of local government. For this reason, the groups closest to local government exert the greatest influence on local code requirements.

These local groups are not normally concerned about the complex technical provisions of codes, but they are vitally interested in the relatively simple provisions that affect their daily lives.

---

[2] A complete listing of these agencies and their mailing addresses is listed in the Appendix.

[3] The National Electrical Code is published by the National Fire Protection Association. (See Appendix.)

They do not question structural design requirements because they do not understand them. They do question leaking roofs, drafty windows and cracked plaster because they have to live with them. Local amendments to model building codes are frequently brought about by the indignant and usually justified complaints of dissatisfied home owners.

Weaknesses in code requirements can only be discovered at the level of enforcement and it is the actual experience of inspectors in the field that provides the feedback necessary to temper and reconcile the theories of the scientists and the claims of industry with the performance level of the tradesmen and the abuse of buildings, intentional or unintentional, by their occupants.

One example will illustrate this point:

A family purchased a $40,000 home in a rapidly expanding prestige suburb. In less than three years, the ceramic tile around the bathtub fell off the wall. This was not an isolated situation; the life expectancy of ceramic tile tub and shower enclosures in that suburb was three to five years. The home owners stormed the city hall and demanded that something be done.

It was. The City Council amended the building code to require that all ceramic wall tile around bathtubs and in shower enclosures be installed on a metal lath and portland cement base.

There are other satisfactory methods that can be used to install ceramic tile, *however, they require strict adherence to manufacturers instructions by the tradesmen* and to post an inspector on every tile installation job was completely impractical.

Amendments of this nature contribute substantially to the non-uniformity of codes and have nurtured the mistaken belief, on the part of some home builders, that a federal building code would solve the problem. Those holding this belief lack understanding of the role of the "Model Codes" as basic documents that set forth minimum requirements.

Except in the larger cities, the basic industries such as steel, lumber, cement and gypsum are not directly involved in local building regulations. Through their trade associations, however, they are the major proponents of changes in the model codes.

The engineers assigned by the major trade associations to work with the model code publishing groups are probably the most knowledgeable resource people in the country as far as model code requirements and procedures for their revision are concerned. These engineers work constantly at the task of keeping the model code requirements up to date as far as their particular industry is concerned. The bulk of their proposals involve the use of new or improved materials and obtaining a better competitive position for their industry.

Since the market areas of the major trade associations are national or international, it is imperative that their materials have uniform acceptance. For this reason, proposals for code changes are processed through all of the model code publishing groups. It may seem cumbersome and inefficient to have to approach four different organizations with the same proposal but it is not as cumbersome as it seems and there is one very important advantage, from industry's standpoint, to this system. A change proposed to one group can be proposed to all except for the code section numbers and, an approval by one group can be used as leverage with another or conversely, disapproval by one group can be used as a basis for reorganizing and redrafting a proposal for another.

Because all of the trade associations are active participants in code change activity, a reasonable balance of competitive position is maintained.

In spite of opposing *individual* interests, the trade association representatives have the *common* interest of dealing with the model code publishing groups. For this purpose they have formed their own organization called the Building Industry Association Representatives (BIAR). BIAR has a unique but unofficial status with the model code publishing groups. It meets with their leadership to discuss code change policies and procedures and its needs and recommendations are usually given favorable consideration. Through informal liaison BIAR strives for uniformity of the procedures used by the building officials organizations in processing proposed code changes.

This group as a whole is well satisfied with the existing code system and is opposed to a Federal building code.

Between the home owners groups at the local level, and the trade associations at the national level, the rest of the groups exert their influence. As with the trade associations, the diverse interests of these groups tend to maintain a reasonable balance in code requirements.

In this chapter we have seen that code requirements are influenced by a multitude of interests, from individual home owners to trade associations representing the nation's largest industries. In Chapter V, we shall examine the *Model Codes* and the part they play in the code system in the United States.

The Model Codes

THE development of the model codes was covered in Chapter I, and in Chapter IV we learned of the influence of individuals and organizations on code requirements. In this chapter, we will look at the model codes as the basis of our nation's code system.

There are five major model code publishing organizations in the United States. Three of these organizations are membership organizations controlled by local government code enforcement officials. These organizations might properly be termed *general interest* groups because their voting members are public officials charged with protecting the public health, safety and general welfare. These organizations are the Building Officials Conference of America (BOCA), the International Conference of Building Officials (ICBO), and the Southern Building Code Congress (SBCC).

The other two organizations by their natures might properly be termed *special* or *limited* interest groups. The membership of the American Insurance Association (AIA) is comprised of capital stock insurance companies. The association's prime mission, and it is a legitimate one, is to reduce fire loss. The National Fire Protection Association (NFPA) has a much broader membership base. It is comprised of some two hundred *organization members,* mostly trade associations and insurance rating bureaus, and twenty-one thousand *associate members.* The latter includes architects, builders, merchants, manufacturers, engineers, fire marshals, fire chiefs, firemen, electricians, credit men, insurance executives, field men, agents, brokers, chambers of commerce, public libraries and many other organizations, individuals, firms and corporations.

The National Fire Protection Association has two functions: one is to make the standards[1] under guidance of which the fire waste may be checked; the other is to educate the people in the observance of those standards and point out the penalties for ignoring them.[2]

Other *special* or *limited* interest groups that publish model technical codes are: The American Society of Mechanical Engineers (ASME), American Society of Heating, Refrigeration and Air Conditioning Engineers (ASHRAE), the International Association of Plumbing and Mechanical Officials (IAPMO), and the American Public Health Association (APHA).

No one organization publishes a comprehensive and compatible set of codes that could be adopted as a package by a local government with reasonable assurance that all areas in need of regulation were adequately covered.

The Building Officials Conference of America is developing a complete code enforcement system however, and expects to publish a Mechanical Code in 1970 that will complete its package. BOCA does not intend to publish an Electrical Code and will continue to defer to the National Electrical Code published by the National Fire Protection Association. BOCA is the only organization besides the American Insurance Association that publishes a Fire Prevention Code.

The nationally recognized model codes and their publishers are listed below:

Building Codes

Basic Building Code..BOCA
National Building Code..AIA
Southern Standard Building Code...SBCC
Uniform Building Code...ICBO

Electrical Codes

National Electrical Code..NFPA

Elevator Codes

Safety Code for Elevators, Dumbwaiters and Escalators......ANSI

---

[1] Some of these standards are published as *codes*. The complete ten volume set of standards is called the National Fire Codes.

[2] National Fire Protection Association, "Objects, Membership and Functions", *1968 Yearbook and Committee List* (Boston: National Fire Protection Association, 1968), p. 2.

Safety Code for Manlifts...ANSI

Fire Prevention Codes

Basic Fire Prevention Code..BOCA
Fire Prevention Code..AIA

Housing Codes

Basic Housing Code...BOCA
Housing Code ....APHA
Southern Standard Housing Code.................................SBCC
Uniform Housing Code..ICBO

Plumbing Codes

Basic Plumbing Code..BOCA
National Plumbing Code..ASME
Southern Standard Plumbing Code...............................SBCC
Uniform Plumbing Code...IAPMO

Miscellaneous Codes

Boiler and Unfired Pressure Vessel Code.................ASME
Flammable Liquids Code...NFPA
Safety Code for Mechanical Refrigeration.................ASHRAE
Safety to Life Code *(formerly Building Exits Code)* ....NFPA

The building code system or non-system that exists in the United States has been under constant criticism for over half a century.

In 1921, the Senate Committee on Reconstruction and Production issued a report in which it was pointed out that building code requirements varied widely, and were one source of unnecessarily high construction costs. Since that time, various writers and speakers have repeated these charges and have also referred to lack of flexibility in dealing with new materials and new methods of construction. Much of this criticism is justified. However, it frequently fails to take into account the great advances that have taken place in codes in recent years, and it constitutes a negative rather than a constructive approach to the problem.[3]

The above is quoted directly from a booklet published by the

----

[3] George N. Thompson, *Preparation and Revision of Building Codes,* U. S. Department of Commerce, National Bureau of Standards, Building Materials and Structures Report BMS 116 (Washington: U. S. Government Printing Office, 1949), p. 2.

39

United States Department of Commerce, September 11, 1949, titled "Preparation and Revision of Building Codes". The purpose of the booklet was to provide local governments with guide lines for writing *their own* building codes.

On December 12, 1968 the National Commission on Urban Problems reported as follows:

> In brief, the facts disclosed by the exhaustive inquiries of this Commission at local, State, and National levels, and the problems faced by producers, builders, and professional people in the building industry, show unmistakably that alarms sounded over the past years about the building code situation have been justified. If anything, the case has been understated. The situation calls for a drastic overhaul, both technically and intergovernmentally.[4]

The degree of uniformity that does exist in the United States today can be attributed directly to the voluntary efforts of the model code publishing organizations.

For many years local governments, encouraged by the Federal Government, believed that building regulations must be *tailor-made* for each municipality. In addition to Preparation and Revision of Building Codes mentioned above, other government publications that have encouraged non-uniformity are:

- Recommended Building Code Requirements for New Dwelling Construction, BMS 88, 1942 superseded by BMS 107, 1947.
- Local Development and Enforcement of Housing Codes, HHFA, 1953.
- Rehabilitation Guide for Residential Properties, HUD PG 50, 1968.
- Basic Housing Inspection, HEW, 1968.
- APHA-PHS Recommended Housing Maintenance and Occupancy Ordinance, HEW, 1969.

It is amazing that, in spite of the Federal Government's encouragement of *do-it-yourself* codes, the Commission on Urban Problems was able to report in December, 1968:

At the national level, the major problems are of a somewhat dif-

---

[4] National Commission on Urban Problems, *Building the American City*, Report of the National Commission on Urban Problems to the Congress and to the President of the United States (Washington: U. S. Government Printing Office, 1968), p. 266.

ferent order. The contents of the four national model building codes—BOCA, ICBO, Southern and National— are more up-to-date and progressive than is generally assumed. Most of the controversial materials and methods of production are now included in their provisions . . .

This is not to say that there are no serious defects in model codes . . .

Nonetheless, the contents of the national model construction codes have at times received more criticism than they deserve, and sometimes the criticism has been unfounded and misinformed. If these codes could be applied over wide geographic areas without amendment, the present chaotic situation would be remarkably improved.[5]

The Commission's investigation of charges that local building codes were a major obstruction to progress in the building industry revealed that 88 per cent of the nation's 4,067 municipalities and townships with a population of 5,000 or more had building codes based on one of the four model codes, a state code or did not have a code. Since the few states that have codes base them on one of the four model codes, it is obvious that the model codes are the backbone of the code system in the United States.

There is good reason to believe that most of the 383 jurisdictions reporting that their local codes are not related to one of the four model codes are so lacking in code knowledge that they are unaware of the original source of their codes' contents. It is reasonably safe to state that practically all of the local building codes in the United States are based on portions of one or more of the four nationally recognized model codes.

The Commission's survey revealed that of the 3,273 jurisdictions over 5,000 in population having building codes, 2,199, or 67 per cent, are based on one of the model codes. Thirty-four out of 48 cities, or 70 per cent of those having populations over 25,000, base their codes on one of the models.[6]

From the statistics above, one might conclude that codes are not the problem they have been purported to be. Unfortunately, that is not the case. The commission asked these questions about lack of uniformity:

What conditions face the local builder, the industrial fabricator,

---

[5] *Ibid.*, p. 265.
[6] *Ibid.*, p. 259.

the mobile home company, or the architect who wishes to build, sell, or design housing or housing products in the metropolitan areas of the United States? Can he market his preassembled plumbing or electrical unit? Can his new product, approved by a model code group, be used locally? Can he obtain approval from the local building code official to sell his factory-built housing unit? Can the pre-assembled panels be installed or must they be ripped apart in order that factory-installed electrical wiring can be inspected? What are the facts with respect to both the requirements and the practices under local codes?

Here are some of the answers that point up the problems:

Each year the national model code groups meet and consider changes and revisions in their codes. While there are complaints about the procedure, the fact is that the model codes are revised from time to time, leading to ultimate acceptance of many—if not the most controversial—new products and methods. Most of the national model codes or their plumbing code or plumbing code chapter counterparts actually allow plastic pipe for drain, waste, or vent; wall board, and Romex cable, to name only a few of the more prominent products which building codes are said to exclude.

But a major complaint is that the codes at the local level, even when based on a national model code, do not provide for the use of such products and new procedures ...

One of the frequent complaints heard by the Commission was that local codes actually bore little relationship to the model construction codes on which they are sometimes said to be based ...

Of the jurisdictions using model codes, only 58 per cent were found to have established procedures for the annual consideration of changes recommended by the code organizations and only 28 per cent had adopted as much as 90 per cent of the recommended changes of the model code groups during the previous three years. Of all jurisdictions having a building construction code of any kind, 45 per cent either had not adopted or comprehensively revised their codes in the previous four years.

Thus, while strong arguments are made concerning the quality of the national model construction codes, the facts are that their provisions do not apply without substantial amendment on a wide-spread basis at the local level ...

The problem of local acceptance of the provisions of the national model codes can be further illustrated by an example. One of the four major national building code groups has an eight member committee which passes on such issues as the use of plastic pipe for inclusion under the provisions of the model code. On the basis of evidence presented to the committee, its members voted unanimously to accept the use of plastic pipe in the drainage system of non-multifamily residential construction. They recommended that such use be incorporated locally as a part of the plumbing chapter provisions of their building code.

Even today, however, the use of plastic pipe for this purpose is allowed under the local code in the jurisdiction of only one of the eight members who voted to include or accept it in the national code.

This example highlights how local practice or local amendment to a code takes precedence over the provisions of a national model code even in those jurisdictions where such a model code is adopted as the basis of the local code.[7]

It also indicates that while local government code enforcement officials serving on code changes committees of national organizations are free to accept new materials and methods, they are unable to overcome the political factors at the local level that maintain and support the vested interests of traditional materials and methods.

The National Commission on Urban Problems' survey of building codes dealt with 17,993 units of local government. Of these, 7,609 were within the standard metropolitan statistical areas of the United States, including 404 counties, 2,228 townships, and 4,977 municipalities. All of the 314 municipalities above 50,000 in population were surveyed. All 404 metropolitan counties were surveyed. Samples of the remaining metropolitan units were taken.

Of the total sample, 10,384 units were outside the standard metropolitan statistical areas. Unlike the units within SMSA's (Standard Metropolitan Statistical Area), those with 1,000 persons or less were omitted. The survey dealt with a sample representing 2,645 counties, 2,732 townships, and 5,007 municipalities outside SMSA's.

Of the almost 18,000 units of government represented in the sample, 46.4 per cent, or just under half, had a building code. Almost 54 per cent had no such code.[8]

Of the 7,609 units of government within SMSA's, 4,527—59.5 per cent—had a building code. More than 40 per cent did not.[9]

---

[7] *Ibid.*, p. 258.

[8] The major criticism of codes has been that they are too restrictive, yet less than half of the local governments in the United States have any codes at all and consequently place no restrictions on builders.

[9] Even in the SMSA's, builders are completely unregulated by building codes in over 40 per cent of local government jurisdictions.

Of the 10,384 units outside SMSA's, only 3,817—36.8 per cent—had a building code.[10]

The survey obtained extensive details on the practices of municipalities and townships, both within and outside SMSA's, which had a population of 5,000 or more. These are the areas where building codes and the provisions of building codes are most important.

There are 4,067 such units of government. Of these, 80.5 per cent (3,273) had a building code. But almost 20 per cent did not.[11]

Local government jurisdictions in the United States having building codes is illustrated in Table 1.

Table 1.—Number and Per Cent of Units of General
Government According to Survey Sample Which Have a Building Code

	Within SMSA's		Outside SMSA's	
	Number	Per Cent	Number	Per Cent
Counties	159	39.4	256	9.7
Municipalities	3,434	69.0	*3,050	*60.9
Townships	934	41.9	*511	*18.7

*Units of under 1,000 omitted.

In addition to a building code for construction, many jurisdictions reported both an electrical code and a plumbing code to cover mechanical work. Of these, The National Electrical Code dominated the electrical code field. The survey showed that of the 3,273 governments which had a building construction code, 78.1 per cent (2,556 units) had also adopted the National Electrical Code.

The National Plumbing Code has been of primary importance in that field. Recently, however, other plumbing codes, such as the BOCA and the Western Plumbing Codes, have become important because of the failure since 1955 to revise the National Plumbing Code.[12] The survey found that the National Plumbing Code was

---

[10] Outside of the SMSA's, builders have almost total freedom to experiment and innovate since 72 per cent of local governments have no building regulations.

[11] One out of five local governments in the United States with populations of over 5,000 allow building construction to go completely unregulated.

[12] BOCA was a sponsor of the National Plumbing Code which is an ANSI standard, however, since ANSI procedures prevented annual updating of the code, BOCA withdrew as a sponsor and published the Basic Plumbing Code, which will be updated annually through democratic procedures.

used by only 43.9 per cent (1,438) of the 3,273 units which had adopted a building construction code. This means that many local governments (2,629, or 65 per cent of all units) either do not have a plumbing code or use the BOCA, Western, or a plumbing code other than the National Plumbing Code.[13]

Excessive Construction Costs
Due to Local Code Requirements

To determine the impact of local building codes on home construction, the Commission undertook a detailed study of code problems confronting manufacturers producing "prefabricated houses".

Their operations were selected for study because they are concerned with the distribution of a product that is more or less uniform and must be approved by building officials within relatively large regions . . .

The study produced findings in the following three categories:

1. An extensive list was assembled indicating specific local code requirements which exceeded those in national model codes and the FHA minimum property standards. The extra costs per house attributed to each of these items ranged from $25 to $640. The list, assembled from 126 reports submitted by 20 home manufacturers, cites code requirements of 32 counties and 109 cities and towns in 20 states.

2. Based on the total list (reported only by those home manufacturers participating in the study), the home manufacturers advisory committee prepared a list of excessive code requirements most frequently encountered by home manufacturers, as shown in Table 2. If a manufacturer were forced to incorporate every item in his product, there would be "extra costs" of $1,838 per house if he marketed in 20 states. The home used for estimating costs was assumed to be a 1,000 square foot family unit that would cost $12,000 without improved lot, under model code or FHA requirements.

3. The most significant information was revealed in an analysis of the problems of one manufacturer who must adjust his product to all codes in the region within which he operates.

The Commission staff analyzed the reports submitted by that manufacturer relating to code requirements of 19 counties and six cities included in the six States of Georgia, Maryland, Kentucky, North Carolina, Virginia, and Ohio, within which the manufacturer

---

[13] National Commission on Urban Problems, *Building the American City*, p. 257.

conducted his business. Within a relatively small market area of 25 code jurisdictions, cited by the manufacturer, there are reported 75 different code requirements considered to be excessive.[14] The reported excessive code items for each one of the 25 individual code jurisdictions ranged in number from one to 13, with extra costs ranging from $50 to $520 per house within each jurisdiction.

If the single manufacturer attempted to produce a standard product which would meet the code requirements of the 25 areas, he would have to introduce 75 separate extra factors in materials and/or methods of construction exceeding the normal requirements in model codes and FHA regulations. The cost of each basic home would thus be raised by $2,492.[15]

The big hurdle, in the opinion of the Commission, is local building codes. What is needed at the local level is a system which provides for:

1. The uniform application of up-to-date building and mechanical codes over an area large enough to allow mass production methods and specialization. At the minimum, such an area should cover any of the major metropolitan areas of the United States such as Greater New York, including the contiguous areas of New Jersey and Connecticut; Chicago and its adjoining counties, including Lake County, Indiana; Greater Los Angeles, including Orange County; St. Louis and the East St. Louis and Madison-St. Clair County industrial complex, and similar areas throughout the country.

2. Minimum standards below which no community might fall and maximum[16] limits in order to prevent restrictive practices. Then the mobile home industry, the prefabricated housing industry, the manufacturers of preassembled plumbing and electrical units, and the producers of new products could be guaranteed an opportunity to build and sell on a competitive price-cost basis provided only that their product or method met minimum standards of performance or specifications established by competent and reliable testing groups through the application of objective standards.

---

[14] The Commission report does not indicate whether these requirements are considered excessive by the Commission staff or by the manufacturer.

[15] National Commission on Urban Problems, *Building the American City,* p. 263.

[16] The one word *maximum* is what all of the noise and shouting about restrictive code requirements is all about. Manufacturers of nationally distributed buildings or building components cannot tolerate the constitutional right of state and local governments to set local minimum standards that are higher than the national minimum standards.

Table 2.—More Frequent Code Requirements in Excess of Model
Codes or FHA Minimum Property Standards

	Extra cost added
Foundation footings to clay, when piers and grade beam would do as well	$ 150.00
Special bolts	15.00
Unnecessary bridging and ties	76.00
Extra number and sizing of joists above FHA requirements	63.00
Conventional floor rather than stress skin floor	40.00
Extra thickness of sub-floor	30.00
Extra sheathing above FHA requirements	125.00
Extra studs above FHA requirements	30.00
Extra window and door headers above FHA requirements	20.00
Extra thickness of gypsum board	22.00
Plaster instead of gypsum board	200.00
Extra fire wall requirements in frame construction above model codes	50.00
Extra roof sheathing ($25-$50)	37.50
Extra roof trusses ($25-$50)	37.50
Requirement of a masonry chimney when a Class B flue would do a better job	150.00
Special fire protection in furnace room not needed when approved heating for zero clearance is used	100.00
Extra plumbing above first floor over National Plumbing Code ($135-$250)	192.00
Extra plumbing below first floor over National Plumbing Code	100.00
Extra electric over National when no conduit	50.00
Extra electric over National when rigid conduit required	300.00
Extra heating duct requirements (return metal plenum over gypsum) and insulation beyond 6 feet from hot air plenum	50.00
Total	$1,838.00

3. An appeals procedure whereby any arbitrary decisions of a local inspector could be appealed quickly and without prejudice to the builder or manufacturer, to a body composed of both competent technical personnel and individuals representing the broad public interest.[17]

The Commission also observed that: "While there are many problems, most of the basic ones do not now lie with the provisions of the model construction codes as such."[18]

Local Governments Benefit from Model Codes

While it is quite evident that some segments of the construction industry are hindered in marketing their products on a nation-wide basis, local governments have reaped a windfall of code know-how through the availability of nationally recognized model codes published and maintained by organizations of code enforcement officials and other experts in the field.

Local governments adopting one of the model codes provide their communities with building regulations having the following advantages:

- *They Provide Sound Regulations.* Based on sound principles of safety and recognizing the difference between standards and regulations, these codes contain only the necessary requirements to provide for the safety of the occupants of buildings and their neighbors. In contrast to the purpose of an architect's or engineer's specifications, they are intended to provide for the general communal good rather than the protection of individual interest.
- *They Establish Performance Requirements.* Instead of specifying in detail the materials to be used and the methods of combining them, these codes state the requirements for the performance that elements of buildings shall produce under the conditions of use, and establish the evaluation formulae or criteria for determining in advance that this performance will be accomplished. This allows the designers full leeway for the expression of ingenuity and frequently results in reducing construction costs.

---

[17] National Commission on Urban Problems, *Building the American City*, p. 265.
[18] *Ibid.*, p. 266.

- *Their Broad Background Results in Unbiased Provisions.* These codes are free from personal prejudices, pressures from local influences and biased recommendations of vested interests. They reflect the combined knowledge and experience of many people in the construction industry, including building officials, architects, engineers and industry specialists.
- *They Encourage the Use of New Ideas.* The method of preparing the code provisions assures the public of reasonable safeguards while permitting the use of new materials and methods of construction that will frequently reduce costs. Reports of the evaluation of new products and systems issued by the code-sponsoring agencies, after careful study of data regarding the behavior of the products, permits acceptance of them by local officials with confidence in their performance.
- *The Use of These Codes Involves Minimum Initial Cost.* The adoption of a prepared recognized code by any local government eliminates the necessity of drafting, typing, duplicating, editing, proofreading and printing which are both time consuming and expensive. The recognized codes are available at nominal cost at much less than the cost of printing comparable quantities by local communities.
- *It Permits Convenient and Economical Upkeep.* Changes approved under the sponsor-organizations' procedure after careful study are made available to help communities keep them up-to-date. When adopted by local governments, these changes bring the advantages of modern regulations to the people of the community.
- *It Secures the Advantages of Uniformity.* By the adoption of the same code by all communities in a metropolitan area, uniformity of regulations can be secured without the sacrifice of individual autonomy by any community. This makes it possible to eliminate the high cost to the public of numerous independent codes in any area.[19]

In this chapter, we have learned of the advantages and the limitations of the model codes. In Chapter VI, we will attempt to answer the question: *Is a Federal Building Code Necessary?*

---

[19] Statement, National Coordinating Council, May 13, 1963.

Chapter

VI

Is a Federal Building Code Necessary?

IN the last chapter, we examined the model codes published by private organizations as the basis of the code system in the United States. We observed that in spite of the fact that the model codes are updated annually and their requirements are substantially the same, vast differences in requirements exist at the local government level where these codes or codes based on them are actually enforced. In this chapter, we shall investigate some of the causes of this lack of uniformity and some of the proposals for correcting the situation. Finally, we shall discuss the feasibility and legality of a Federal Building Code.

Authority for Codes

The development, administration, and enforcement of building and other regulatory codes has traditionally been delegated to local governments.

The authority under which a local government formulates and administers building codes is the police power of the State—that is, the power of a sovereign government in a Federal union to legislate for the public health, safety, morals, and general welfare. *Under the Constitution of the United States, the police power resides in the States*; and though it is permissible for the States to delegate various police power functions to localities, the localities exercise these functions as agents of the State and not by virtue of any inherent powers of their own.[1]

---

[1] National Commission on Urban Problems, *Building the American City*, Report of the National Commission on Urban Problems to the Congress and to the President of the United States (Washington: U. S. Government Printing Office, 1968), p. 260.

In addition to delegating the responsibility for developing and enforcing building regulations to local governments, *the states themselves pass laws and adopt regulations that frequently overlap and conflict with local codes.* Serious problems exist because of the multiplicity of State Laws and enforcement agencies that concern themselves with structural, fire protection, exit and similar requirements in buildings occupied as tenement houses, nursing homes, day care nurseries, hospitals, schools, places of public assembly, factories and many others. The maze of conflicting jurisdictions between state and local governments is a cross borne by architects, engineers and the general public in almost every state.

> With regard to the Federal Government, it is estimated that at least 35 different agencies are directly or indirectly concerned with construction. The standards which they insist upon differ from agency to agency and from department to department. The chaos which exists between and among Federal Government groups mirrors the greater problem of building codes in the nation. But it ill behooves the Federal Government and Federal agencies to preach to states, localities and model code groups until they move to put their own house in order.[2]

In order to reach some conclusions about the feasibility and legality of a Federal Building Code, it seems appropriate to list the highlights of a half century of code criticism chronologically.

1920

A Senate Committee concluded: The building codes of the country have not been developed upon scientific data, but rather on compromise; they are not uniform in principle and in many instances, involve an additional cost of construction without assuring most useful or more durable buildings.[3]

1922

Secretary of Commerce Herbert Hoover reported to Congress that conflicting and antiquated building codes were

[2] *Ibid.*, p. 266.
[3] Advisory Commission on Intergovernmental Relations, *Building Codes: A Program for Intergovernmental Reform*, A Report Prepared by the Advisory Commission on Intergovernmental Relations (Washington, D.C.: U. S. Government Printing Office, 1966), p. 2.

increasing construction costs in the United States by from 10 per cent to 20 per cent.[4]

1951

The Chamber of Commerce of the United States recommended that support be given to the four nationally recognized model building codes and that states adopt enabling legislation permitting the adoption of model codes by reference.[5]

1958

House and Home magazine reported that a conference of some 70 home building experts had declared that "chaos and confusion of conflicting local codes is costing home buyers an average of at least $1,000 a house."[6]

1963

American Builder magazine devoted its March issue to "The Code Problem and What to Do About It." The theme of this issue was that one national building code was the answer.[7]

1964

The Chamber of Commerce of the United States[8] reiterated its support of the *model codes* with the statement:

"Clearly, model building codes offer the best means for obtaining building regulations which meet all tests of effectiveness and economy."[9]

---

[4] *Ibid.*

[5] Chamber of Commerce of The United States, *Building Codes and Construction Progress* (Washington, D.C.: Chamber of Commerce of the United States, 1951) , p. 16.

[6] Advisory Commission on Intergovernmental Relations, *Building Codes: A Program for Intergovernmental Reform,* p. 2.

[7] The Code Problem and What to Do About It", *American Builder,* March, 1963.

[8] The Chamber of Commerce of the United States should not be confused with the United States Department of Commerce which is an agency of the Federal Government.

[9] Chamber of Commerce of the United States, *Building Codes for Community Development and Construction Progress* (Washington, D.C.: Chamber of Commerce of the United States, 1964) , p. 15.

1965

The "La Que Committee"[10] formally known as the "Panel on Engineering and Commodity Standards of the Commerce Technical Advisory Board" recommended that a *uniform national code* be made available for voluntary adoption by local governments but with the provision that the technical requirements in the code could not be changed, regardless of local conditions. The report did not suggest that the adoption of this *uniform national code* be promoted by the Federal Government nor that the code be developed by the Federal Government. It did, however, suggest that this "be undertaken under the supervision and with the guidance of the National Bureau of Standards for subsequent promulgation by the 'Institute' as a USA Code."[11]

1966

The Advisory Commission on Intergovernmental Relations[12] called for a major overhaul and restructuring

---

[10] The "La Que Committee" was a panel appointed by J. Herbert Holloman who was Assistant Secretary of Commerce for Science and Technology. Mr. Holloman had proposed a "Civilian Technology Program" several years earlier to bolster the "lagging building industry" and certain other industries. Congress denied funds for the program, however, and later reprimanded the Department of Commerce for attempting to accomplish its objectives through organization within the Bureau of Standards. This panel was instructed to study the broad requirements for standards and the activities related thereto in the United States and to make a recommendation on its findings in regard thereto, specifically "as to activities important to meeting national requirements for standards with particular emphasis on the role of the Federal Government and the Department of Commerce" in these activities. The panel was headed by Dr. Francis L. La Que, Vice President of the International Nickle Company. Dr. A. Allen Bates, Chief of the Building Research Division of the National Bureau of Standards, a federal agency, served as secretary. The Managing Director of the American Standards Association (now the American National Standards Institute), and the Executive Secretary of the American Society for Testing and Materials, were the only representatives from standards or code activities serving on the panel. Other members of the panel were from private industry or Federal Government bureaus.

[11] Paul E. Baseler, *Federal Activities,* A Report on Developments in The Federal Government Affecting Building Codes and Administration (Chicago: Building Officials Conference of America, Inc., 1965).

[12] The Advisory Commission on Intergovernmental Relations is a 26 member permanent bipartisan body set up by an Act of Congress. It is made up of governors, mayors, county officials, state legislators and representatives of Congress, the Executive Branch, and the general public.

of intergovernmental responsibilities for building codes to meet the nation's housing and commercial construction needs. Its report, "Building Codes: A Program for Intergovernmental Reform" contained a number of major findings and recommendations aimed at building code modernization, uniformity and improved local administration.

1968

The National Commission on Urban Problems[13] (The

[13] The National Commission on Urban Problems was responsible both to the President and to the Congress. The preface to *Bldg. the American City* explains that President Johnson named the Chairman and members on January 12, 1967, and said the Commission's charter was two-fold: "First: to work with the Department of Housing and Urban Development and conduct a penetrating review of zoning, housing and building codes, taxation and development standards. These processes have not kept pace with the times. Stunting growth and opportunity, they are the springboards from which many of the ills of urban life flow.

Second: to recommend the solutions, particularly those ways in which the efforts of the Federal Government, private industry, and local communities can be marshaled to increase the supply of low-cost decent housing."

Congress described the purposes and needs for the study as follows: "The Congress finds that the general welfare of the nation requires that local authorities be encouraged and aided to prevent slums, blight, and sprawl, preserve natural beauty, and provide for decent, durable housing so that the goal of a decent home and a suitable living environment for every American family may be realized as soon as feasible. The Congress further finds that there is a need to study housing and building codes, zoning, tax policies, and development standards in order to determine how (1) local property owners and private enterprise can be encouraged to serve as large a part as they can of the total housing and building need, and (2) Federal, state and local governmental assistance can be so directed as to place greater reliance on local property owners and private enterprise and enable them to serve a greater share of the total housing and building need."

The statement above is part of Section 301 of the Housing and Urban Development Act of 1965 which also directed that a specific study be made of:

"...the structure of (1) state and local urban and suburban housing and building laws, standards, codes, and regulations and their impact on housing and building costs, how they can be supplied, improved, and enforced, at the local level, and what methods might be adopted to promote more uniform building codes and the acceptance of technical innovations including new building practices and materials; (2) state and local zoning and land use laws, codes, and regulations, to find ways by which states and localities may improve and utilize them in order to obtain further growth and development; and (3) Federal, state, and local tax policies with respect to their effect on land and property cost and on incentives to build housing and make improvements in existing structures."

Douglas Commission) [14] recommended that: *"Unless all else fails, we should not seek a national code imposed by the Federal government. Instead, we need national standards developed by both private and public bodies which can be universally accepted and applied."* [15]

The President's Committee on Urban Housing (the Kaiser Committee) [16] reported that: "In the judgment of our staff and consultants, the Federal government appears to have the power to promulgate a uniform national building code under the Commerce Clause of the U. S. Constitution. *This committee, however, has little enthusiasm for adoption of uniform national codes."* [17]

Who Sustains the Clamor for a Federal Building Code?

For half a century, the cries for a Federal Building Code have waxed hot and cold or at least warm and cool. Who maintains the incessant demand that the Federal government is the only logical overseer of our nation's building regulations?

It should be obvious by now that the drive for a Federal Building Code is residual within the United States Department of Commerce. Even in the face of a Congressional reprimand, the Department has pursued its own singular course.

In his new book, "The Age of Discontinuity" Peter F. Drucker of New York University, an expert on government, says that government agencies are all becoming "autonomous" and are "ends in themselves, and directed by their own desire for power, their own narrow vision, rather than by national policy." [18]

The tenacity with which the Department of Commerce has

---

[14] During its existence, the Commission was commonly called the "Douglas Commission" after its Chairman, former Illinois Senator Paul H. Douglas.

[15] National Commission on Urban Problems, *Building the American City*, Report of the National Commission on Urban Problems to the Congress and to the President of the United States (Washington: U. S. Government Printing Office, 1968), p. 254.

[16] The Committee was chaired by Edgar F. Kaiser.

[17] President's Committee on Urban Housing, *A Decent Home*, Report of the President's Committee on Urban Housing (Washington, D.C.: U. S. Government Printing Office, 1968), p. 28.

[18] "Big Government—Is It Out of Hand?", *U.S. News & World Report*, March 24, 1969, pp. 28-30.

been able to cling to its ancient goal is best illustrated by the following quotation:

> What most plainly reveals the independent power of the bureaucracy are those cases where the bureaucrats of some department, agency or office persist in a policy that is contrary to the policy held by both Congress and the President. Under such circumstances —which are not at all unusual—it is obviously an illusion to believe that the civil servants are in reality subject to the 'policy-making' appointive official who is their nominal superior, or to the laws that have been enacted by Congress. In a process well known to modern Washington, the official, who may be the secretary or assistant secretary of one of the major departments, becomes the dupe or tool or front of the permanent civil servants whom he is assigned to direct . . . The independent policy of the bureaucracy is manifest in connection not only with the general issue of statism but with a multitude of other problems as well, some of them minor and accidental, perhaps springing from no more complex cause than the ingrained ideas of a long lasting individual bureaucrat or a particular bureau's fossilized work habits.[19]

The Commerce Department's obsession with writing a Federal Building Code might properly be attributed to bureaucratic incest.

What Is Needed?

What is needed to allow full utilization of unique design concepts, innovations and new materials?

While the La Que Committee and the Advisory Commission on Intergovernmental Relations reports advocated a single national code, the more recent reports of the Douglas Commission and Kaiser Committee do not.

It is significant that all of these investigations have pointed up one common problem; local governments have a constitutional right, through the police powers delegated to them by the states, to promulgate and enforce their own building regulations. Local governments, for a multitude of reasons ranging from sheer ignorance and undue influence by special interest groups to

---

[19]James Burnham, "Some Administrators Unkindly View Congress", *Public Administration: Readings in Institutions, Processes, Behavior,* eds. Robert T. Golembiewski, Frank Gibson and Goeffry Y. Cornog (Chicago: Rand McNally & Company, 1965), pp. 75-76.

legitimate concern for the public health, safety, morals, and general welfare have adopted building regulations (codes) that are, even when based on a nationally recognized model, unique to their own jurisdiction.

What, then, can be done insofar as codes are concerned to maximize the construction potential of the United States? Let us examine the recommendations of the Advisory Commission on Intergovernmental Relations (ACIR) and the National Commission on Urban Problems (Douglas Commission).

Advisory Commission on Intergovernmental Relations

Recommendation No. 1. National Program for Performance Standards Development:

The Commission recommends that the Congress authorize and finance an immediate cooperative program, drawing upon recognized public and private efforts, designed to develop national performance criteria and standards testing procedures for building construction.

Recommendation No. 2. National Program for Building Construction Research:

The Commission further recommends that a continuing national program of building research be established to:

(a) identify and define areas within the building field requiring research;

(b) fill gaps in existing knowledge through encouragement and support of research;

(c) formulate a continuing program for the integration and continuity of knowledge and experience; and

(d) provide for demonstration projects that would contribute significantly to building technology.

The Commission also recommends that the President direct Federal agencies having major policy or program responsibilities for construction, urban development and renewal, and associated activities, to cooperate in the developing of knowledge applicable to the solution of building problems.

Recommendation No. 3. State Research and Information Efforts in Building Construction:

The Commission urges that programs for research in building construction be established by appropriate state agencies and institutions of higher education and that appropriate technical

58

information services be established for the dissemination of research findings to public officials and private businesses. Such research and information programs should be carried on within the context of a continuing national research effort recommended above.

Recommendation No. 4. Development of a Model Code by a National Commission:

The Commission recommends that the President either appoint a drafting group representing all levels of government to develop a model code with the participation of the model code groups and other interested public and private groups or, in the event the Temporary National Commission on Codes, Zoning, Taxation and Development Standards[20] is established in accordance with the President's 1965 message on cities to Congress, the Commission's charge be expanded to include a similar assignment. In its report to the President, the code-writing group should recommend appropriate permanent machinery for keeping the code revised and up-to-date and as well as a products approval program to certify new products as to their conformance with code provisions.

Recommendation No. 5. Uniform Standards for Federal Construction:

The Commission recommends that the President instruct all departments and agencies with direct responsibility for building construction, such as the General Services Administration and the Department of Defense, or with responsibility for establishing standards governing construction under programs administered by them, such as the Federal Housing Administration and the Farmers Home Administration, to develop and use a common set of standards to the greatest extent possible.

Recommendation No. 6. Development of a State Model Building Code:

The Commission recommends that the states enact legislation authorizing and directing a state agency to prepare and promulgate a comprehensive model building code with a products approval procedure for permissive adoption by local political subdivisions. The state enabling legislation should specify that local jurisdictions may not alter the model code except on specific approval of the state agency and should establish an appellate body to hear appeals from decisions of adopting local jurisdictions on the application of the code. To

---

[20] The Commission was appointed with a broadened scope and charge as The National Commission on Urban Problems (The Douglas Commission).

the extent possible, state model codes should adhere to nationally recognized models. The Commission urges the adoption of such a state model code by local governments.

The Commission encourages state and local governments to make full use of funds available under section 701 of the Housing Act of 1954 to undertake studies, and other activities necessary for adoption of the model code.

The Commission recommends that those government agencies at the state and local levels responsible for operating and construction programs incorporate the standards of the state model code as their rules and regulations for public construction.

To encourage uniformity in building codes, the Commission further recommends that states consider legislation establishing a uniform policy of conditioning loans and grants to local governments upon conformance of aided projects to the state model code.[21]

Recommendation No. 7. Establishment of a State Construction Review Agency to Develop State-wide Standards Through an Appeals Procedure:

In order to provide for the establishment of uniform state standards governing building construction through an evolutionary process as the need arises, the Commission recommends that states enact legislation creating a building construction review agency at the state level or consider appeals by affected parties from the decisions of local government. Through its decisions, the review agency would establish uniform interpretation of standards.

Recommendation No. 8. Enabling Legislation for Local Adoption by Reference of Model Codes:

The Commission recommends that the states pass appropriate legislation: (a) enabling local jurisdictions to adopt a recognized uniform building code by reference; (b) permitting local jurisdictions to adopt future changes made in such recognized model codes by administrative rather than legislature action.[22]

---

[21] This is the "coercion" method presently in use by many Federal agencies to force their bureaucratic will on state and local governments.

[22] The Commission reiterated its position set forth in the report *Metropolitan Social and Economic Disparities: Implications for Intergovernmental Relations in Central Cities and Suburbs*, adopted in 1965, that the states enact "...legislation authorizing the adoption of uniform...building...codes within metropolitan areas and action by local governments to utilize such authority."

Recommendation No. 9. State Licensing of Building Inspectors:

The Commission recommends that a state supervisory agency be empowered to establish professional qualifications for building inspectors and license candidates as to their fitness for employment on the basis of examinations given by it, or of examination satisfactory to it given by a state or local agency. The state agency should be able to revoke licenses for good and sufficient cause.

States may wish to provide a state salary supplement for local building code inspectors to compensate for the higher salary requirements that would result from the licensing program.

Recommendation No. 10. Training Programs for Building Inspectors:

The Commission recommends the enactment of state legislation authorizing and supporting the training of building inspectors including provision for cooperative arrangements among state agencies, educational institutions and the appropriate building officials organizations in planning and conducting pre-entry courses of study, and providing or arranging for regular internship training programs. The Commission recommends that grants to states and local governments available under Title VIII of the Housing Act of 1964 be utilized by state and local governments to develop training programs for inspectors.[23]

Recommendation No. 11. Provision of Local Building Inspection Services:

The Commission recommends that the state legislature establish, or authorize the state supervisory agency to establish minimum staffing requirements for building inspection[24] in all local government jurisdictions, authorize local governments to enter into interlocal agreements for building inspection services to meet such minimum requirements and empower a state agency to provide both direct and reimbursable building inspection services to local governments.

In order to achieve the most efficient use of available trained and qualified manpower, on-site construction inspection services should be centralized to the extent feasible among the various state and local agencies administering any of the building construction and mechanical codes.[25]

---

[23] This has been done in a few states but should be greatly expanded.

[24] The term "building inspection" is used in the broad sense by the Commission throughout its report; it includes plumbing, electrical and other specialty inspections.

[25] Advisory Commission on Intergovernmental Relations, *Building Codes: A Program For Intergovernmental Reform*, pp. 84-101.

National Commission on Urban Problems

Recommendation No. 1. Framework for development and furtherance of building standards and technology:

The Commission recommends the establishment of the National Institute of Building Sciences as a constituent body in the National Academy of Sciences—National Academy of Engineering. The express purposes of the Institute would be to formulate and/or approve standards for the construction of buildings; provide a mechanism for testing and approving technological innovations; provide a system for evaluating experiences of public and private programs affecting building; provide for research in building technology; assemble and disseminate technical data relating to standards and building technology.

1(a). Formulation of building standards:

The Commission recommends that Congress appropriate at least $5 million to support the National Institute of Building Sciences for a stipulated three-year project. The purposes of the project would be first to review existing standards regulating the construction of building and, second, to prepare and issue uniform building standards based on current knowledge and the most advanced technical criteria for application in Federal, state, and local regulations.

1(b). Provision for performance standards, product approval, and information exchange:

The Commission recommends that Congress authorize an annual Federal appropriation to the National Institute of Building Sciences for the following purposes:

aa. To develop and/or approve test criteria and performance standards, and to supervise research in the examination of building materials, construction methods, and plumbing and electrical and mechanical systems;

bb. To provide a system to test and accept new building materials and equipment, and construction methods;

cc. To provide for the collection and dissemination of available technical data and information relating to the building industry; and

dd. To provide for a system for evaluating experiences of public and private programs affecting building.

Recommendation No. 2

2(a). Use of Federal influence to curb restrictive building code provisions:

The Commission recommends amendment of congressional authorizations for water and sewer and other appropriate facility grants to provide as a condition of eligibility for such grants that building codes in communities receiving such grant assistance shall not be more restrictive than nationally recognized model code standards and subsequently the building code standards to be developed by the National Institute of Building Sciences.

2(b). Formulation of building code standards for rehabilitation housing:

The Commission recommends that Congress authorize the Secretary of Housing and Urban Development to develop model standards to be incorporated in *local* building codes[26] with special reference to the rehabilitation of existing housing.

2(c). Eliminating unnecessary variations in Federal construction standards:

The Commission recommends that the President initiate vigorous action to review the variations in standards used by Federal agencies in direct Federal construction, standards based upon nationally recognized current model codes, and subsequently the standards to be developed by the National Institute of Building Sciences.

Recommendation No. 3. Adoption of state building codes and mandating building code uniformity in metropolitan areas:

The Commission recommends the enactment of state legislation providing for the adoption of state building codes dealing with human occupancy, conforming to nationally recognized model code standards developed and/or approved by the proposed National Institute of Building Sciences recommended earlier. *We further recommend that such state legislation provide that within one year following the adoption of the state code, the provisions of such code shall be applicable without modification throughout each metropolitan area of the state which fails to adopt such nationally recognized standards.*[27]

---

[26] This recommendation would appear to be an encouragement of the continuance of local building codes.

[27] Metropolitan areas, as such, are not political subdivisions of the state and, therefore, have no inherent legal authority. Apparently one recalcitrant minor local government could cause the state code to become mandatory in a major Central City.

Recommendation No. 4. Strengthening state supervision over building code administration:

The Commission recommends that states enact legislation providing for (a) state-wide training and licensing programs of local building inspectors, (b) technical assistance to local governments, and (c) state-wide appeals mechanisms for reconciling differences arising through code interpretation at the local level.[28]

Summary of Recommendations

Although these two commissions subdivided their recommendations differently, the combined recommendations of both can be summarized as follows:

1. There should be a national program for development and furtherance of building standards and technology.
2. There should be development of a model code and/or model code standards by a national commission.
3. All federal agencies should be required to use the same uniform standards for building construction.
4. States should adopt a mandatory state building code based on and not more restrictive than one of the existing nationally recognized model codes and should not permit local governments to alter the model code without state approval.
5. States should adopt enabling legislation permitting local governments to adopt nationally recognized model codes by reference and provide for the adoption of future changes by administrative means.
6. States should establish appeals boards to reconcile local government code interpretations.
7. States should establish product approval procedures.
8. States should have research programs and provide technical assistance to local governments.
9. States should conduct training programs for building inspectors and code enforcement administrators.
10. States should examine and license building inspectors and code enforcement administrators.

---

[28] National Commission on Urban Problems, *Building the American City,* pp. 266-270.

11. States should adopt legislation authorizing local governments to enter into interlocal agreements for building inspection services and should establish or authorize a state agency to provide such services.

Analysis of the Recommendations

Based on the belief that the findings of these two commissions were accurate and their conclusions logical, let us examine their recommendations.

Before beginning an item by item analysis, however, it seems proper to observe that only one recommendation deals directly with the *building code* itself. All of the other recommendations deal with the use, or misuse and abuse, if you prefer, of codes and their ancillary effects. It should also be noted, although it is obvious, that some of the recommendations are conflicting.

There should be a National Program for development and furtherance of building standards and technology. *Why not?* We can never know all there is to know about anything. Look what has been accomplished in our space program in just a few years. Private industry continually conducts research and development projects where there is a possibility of recovering costs and realizing a profit within the foreseeable future, but it cannot be expected to pour millions of dollars of stockholders' money into projects that do not anticipate a return on the investment. *In those areas of required research that are neglected by private industry for lack of a profit incentive, only the Federal Government can fill the gap.*

There should be Development of a Model Code and/or Model Code Standards by a National Commission. *The Model Code. Why? Model Code Standards. Why not?*

The Model Code

In 1905, there was one model building code in the United States. By 1950, there were four. Without constitutional amendment, a Federal Building Code could be nothing more than a fifth *model code*. Local governments could, and would, impose requirements that were more stringent than the Federal code. And this is exactly the problem that our nation's home building industry is attempting to overcome.

At this writing, the publishing organizations of all four model building codes, AIA, BOCA, ICBO and SBCC, have joined hands in developing a comprehensive construction code for one-and two-family dwellings that will be compatible with the general building code published by each group. A national public hearing was held in July of 1969 and it is hoped that the code will be published early in 1970.

Once published, this code will be updated annually through democratic procedures open to all interested parties. The code was developed at no cost to the Federal Government and will be kept up-to-date on the same basis.

Since the home building industry, through the National Association of Home Builders (NAHB), provided the impetus for the development of this code, it is hoped that many of their code problems will be solved by its publication.

In a paper prepared for the Department of Housing and Urban Development (HUD), Douglas E. Parsons, former Chief of the Building Research Division of the National Bureau of Standards, made the following observations:

> There is no evidence that a national code would minimize the major defects of the present code system. Progress in improving the quality of national standards would not be increased thereby, needed new standards would not be supplied, the training of staffs for building officials would not be improved, and the writing of the code would not provide the research data needed for marked progress in developing performance codes and standards. Therefore, emphasis on the plan to write a national building code seems misplaced if the purpose, as sometimes stated, is to achieve better, as well as more, uniform requirements and to prepare performance requirements to the extent feasible. That is, concentrating attention on the conspicuous project of drafting and promulgating a national code would not by itself result in a solution of the existing problems of inadequate codes and standards and it would tend to draw attention away from projects of basic concern. It seems certain that a comprehensive study of the entire system of codes and standards would disclose the need for many programs of research and standardization.

> If one of the model codes were suddenly adopted, with appropriate administrative and technical requirements for the agency and the locality, by all of the code enforcing jurisdictions in the USA, including the Federal agencies, the states and the local communities, some benefits might be noted. But most of the potential benefits of a comprehensive standardization program would not

result from such an event. There would be little or no improvement in the extent to which owners of buildings would be free from annoyances from the lack of interchangeability of parts, because the parts that seem most troublesome are not specified in detail by building codes. New and improved standards for products would be needed to achieve the desired interchangeability. Nor would the general adoption of a national code improve the quality of standards for materials, products or systems.

Producers of building products call attention to advantages of multiple model codes, each under the jurisdiction of a different organization. Smaller groups usually respond to applications for approval more rapidly than larger groups; discussions in smaller groups are apt to be less formal and decisions are made sooner. Moreover, a sponsor may apply to more than one organization, thereby increasing the probability of prompt and decisive action. Some producers feel that a national code could become a mandatory code for any construction in which the Federal Government had an interest. They seem to prefer the present system with the four model codes, the standards of several governmental agencies, etc.

The writing of a national code would require the assistance of experts from many organizations, especially those that have demonstrated their competence in the writing and maintaining of codes and standards. And if a national code were to compete with the existing model codes, it would decrease the effectiveness of these organizations in code-writing and the administration of the codes and in providing services to the local communities. Other means would have to be created to provide these important services. An effective means would be needed also for maintaining any national code. Under the present system, the stimulas of competition between the code-writing organizations assists in assuring reasonably prompt consideration of a proposed revision. No suitable substitute for this competition is obvious.

Agencies of the Federal Government have an outstandingly good record of competence in the drafting and maintaining of standards for items and services which are of major importance to the responsible agency. Otherwise their record is not praiseworthy. In many instances, fault for the poor record does not lie with the agency and its staff. Changes in high-level policies and acts of the Congress often have interrupted programs of standardization that had been highly productive and successful. For example, in one instance the Congress transferred the responsibilities for each of several standardization programs from each of several agencies to a single agency. This centralization of a large group of these programs in one agency seemed desirable and it probably would have led to improvements in efficiency if the agency being given the additional assignment had been provided with the needed additional funds. It was not, and many of the standards became obsolete. In view of the history of governmental standardization programs, exclusive dependence upon the Federal Government to maintain a national standard or code for the building industry does not seem to be an ideal arrangement.[29]

Model Code Standards

In Chapter III, we learned that most of the standards used in building codes are developed by or at the request and sponsorship of the industry most vitally concerned and in Chapter II, we learned that some code requirements were based on the best judgement of experts in the field because no objective standards have been developed. Height and Area limitations were used as an example of this situation. No one industry can expect to profit from the research necessary to the development of a standard covering this important subject and, therefore, there is little likelihood that such a standard will be developed unless the project is undertaken by an agency of the Federal Government.

It would appear desirable for the Model Code Standardization Council (MCSC) [30] to identify all of those areas in code requirements where standards are lacking and press for the research necessary to their development.

All Federal agencies should be required to use the same uniform standards for building construction.

The logic of this is so obvious that it hardly warrants comment except for the fact that it will probably be a very difficult accomplishment.

States should adopt a mandatory state building code based on and not more restrictive than one of the existing nationally recognized model codes and should not permit local governments to alter the model code without state approval.

---

[29] Douglas E. Parsons, *Building Codes and the Producers of Building Products* (Washington: The Producers Council, Inc., 1967) , pp. 10-11.

[30] The Model Code Standardization Council will be discussed in Chapter VIII.

The comments of Mr. Parsons on this recommendation point up the possible pitfalls to this approach:

Control over building design and construction by state governments has been increasing in recent years. There is evidence indicating that some of the expected benefits of the building industry have not resulted from the enactment of state regulations. The achievement of uniformity in codes within a locality is made more difficult by mandatory state codes when the locality includes more than one state. As many metropolitan areas are on the borders of states, diversity in mandatory requirements of states tend to increase the diversity of codes in these localities. There and elsewhere, state regulations also tend to be confusing if they duplicate or relate to subjects covered by the local codes.

Experience has shown that state codes have not been of uniformly high technical merit and that the national model codes have kept pace with advances in technology better than some of the state codes. Funds available to the agencies of state governments which prepare and enforce codes are apt to fluctuate with changes of administrations and to be subject to influence by political considerations.

Finally, like some of the local governments, the authority to enforce building regulations usually is divided among several different agencies and officials of a state so that plans for new construction must be approved by the staff of each agency. Procedures for obtaining approval tend to be dissimilar in the different agencies, and inspectors of the agencies must be dealt with separately. Thus the cost to the builder before and during construction is increased. Producers of building products may have somewhat similar problems if the product must be approved by more than one agency of the state as well as by the local officials. It seems clear, therefore, that increasing the number of state codes would not lead automatically to improvements in codes or in their administration.[31]

States should adopt enabling legislation permitting local governments to adopt nationally recognized model codes by reference and provide for the adoption of future changes by administrative means.

The Douglas Commission report appears to give credence to this recommendation.

What is needed at the local level is a system which provides for:

1. The uniform application of up-to-date building and mechanical codes over an area large enough to allow mass production

---

[31] Parsons, p. 6.

methods and specialization. At the minimum, such an area should cover any of the major metropolitan areas of the United States such as Greater New York, including the contiguous areas of New Jersey and Connecticut; Chicago and its adjoining counties, including Lake County, Indiana; Greater Los Angeles including Orange County; St. Louis and the East St. Louis and Madison-St. Clair County industrial complex and similar areas throughout the country.

2. Minimum standards below which no community might fall and maximum limits in order to prevent restrictive practices. Then the mobile home industry, the pre-fabricated housing industry, the manufacturers of preassembled plumbing and electrical units, and the producers of new products could be guaranteed an opportunity to build and sell on a competitive price-cost basis provided only that their product or method met minimum standards of performance or specifications established by competent and reliable testing groups through the application of objective standards.

3. An appeals procedure whereby any arbitrary decisions of a local inspector could be appealed quickly, and without prejudice to the builder or manufacturer, to a body composed of both competent technical personnel and individuals representing the broad public interest.[32]

States should establish appeals boards to reconcile local government code interpretations.

On this subject, the Douglas Commission report says:

...the States should provide an appeals procedure, not dominated by either a single person, or groups and narrow factions within industry.[33]

In all but the smallest states this would be a cumbersome, time consuming and costly arrangement. It would seem unnecessary if there were a local appellate body as recommended above. Since decisions of administrative appellate bodies may be appealed to the courts, this would appear to be merely another remedy that would have to be exhausted before court appeal.

States should establish product approval procedures.

Compliance with this recommendation would result in an unnecessary duplication of the services already provided by Under

---

[32] National Commission on Urban Problems, *Building the American City,* p. 265.
[33] *Ibid.*

writers' Laboratories, The American Gas Association, The Building Officials Conference of America, The International Conference of Building Officials, The Southern Building Code Congress and other non-profit organizations.[34] *It would further fragmentize the system and impose undue hardship on manufacturers attempting to market building materials on a regional or national basis.*

States should have research programs and provide technical assistance to local governments.

Necessary research that is not being conducted by private industry should be referred to the proposed National Institute of Building Sciences recommended by the Douglas Commission. *There is no need for the citizens of each of the fifty states to bear the cost of an elaborate research facility.*

The technical resources of the states, especially those of the State Universities, should be coordinated and made available to local governments.

States should conduct training programs for building inspectors and code enforcement administrators.

This is the area (code enforcement) that needs the greatest amount of attention and it is one that the states, through their control of the educational system, are best suited to handle. Both pre-entry and post-entry training programs are required. The Building Officials Conference of America sponsors a five-day short course at the University of Illinois. The ongoing three-year curriculum attracted 177 building officials from 35 states the first year (1968) and over 200 the second. Rutgers, the State University of New Jersey, has conducted highly successful programs for building officials for several years. BOCA also sponsors the New England Institute for Building Officials. Now in its eighth year, the Institute which started at the University of Connecticut, is held at the University of Massachusetts.

Most criticism of our code system has been with local practices. Only education and training, with the consequent upgrading of code enforcement personnel, can correct that situation.

States should examine and license building inspectors and code enforcement administrators.

They certainly should. Architects, engineers and many build-

---

[34] The Research and Approvals Programs of the building officials organizations will be explained in Chapter VIII.

ing tradesmen are licensed by the states. Why should public officials charged with protecting the public health, safety and general welfare be exempt from providing satisfactory evidence of their competence?

There could be danger in a licensing law, however, if the examining board were dominated either by trade union representatives or design professionals (architects and engineers). *No one should automatically be issued a license as an inspector or code enforcement administrator by virtue of possession of a trade or professional license or registration in a related field.*

The reason for this is best explained by Thorstein Veblen's concept of "trained incapacity".

Trained incapacity refers to that state of affairs in which one's abilities function as inadequacies or blind spots. Actions based upon training and skills which have been successfully applied in the past may result in inappropriate responses under changed conditions. An inadequate flexibility in the application of skills, will, in a changing milieu, result in more or less serious maladjustments. In general, one adopts measures in keeping with one's past training and under new conditions which are not recognized as significantly different, the very soundness of this training may lead to the adoption of the wrong procedures. In Kenneth Burke's almost echolalic phrase, "people may be unfitted by being fit in an unfit fitness"; their training may become an incapacity.[35]

John W. Gardner, former Secretary of Health, Education and Welfare, made the following statements:

In a world that is rocking with change, we need more than anything else a high capacity for adjustment to changed circumstances, a capacity for innovation. . . .It is not just technical competence which is needed. A society such as ours is dependent upon many kinds of achievement, many kinds of complex understanding. It requires large numbers of individuals with depth of judgement, perspective and a broad comprehension of the problems facing our world.[36]

Nothing contributes more damagingly to the unemployment of educated talent than rigid specialization and rigid attitudes supporting this specialization.[37]

---

[35] Robert K. Merton, "Bureaucratic Structure and Personality", *A Sociological Reader on Complex Organizations*, ed. Amitai Etzioni (New York: Holt, Rinehart and Winston, Inc., 1969), p. 50.

[36] John W. Gardner, *Excellence: Can We Be Equal and Excellent Too?* (New York: Harper & Row, 1961), p. 35.

[37] *Ibid.*, p. 43.

More than a few mayors and city managers have had the unfortunate experience of appointing people who were well qualified as architects, engineers or building tradesmen to responsible positions in code enforcement, only to find that their narrow training and perspectives rendered them completely incapable of administering building regulations.

States should adopt legislation authorizing local governments to enter into interlocal agreements for building inspection services and should establish or authorize a state agency to provide such services.

Both of these recommendations are a must. Small communities cannot afford a fully staffed building department, however, two or three could work out reciprocal arrangements and counties or councils of government could provide inspection services on a contract basis as could the central cities.

States having building codes should provide inspection services in all areas of the state that have not provided in some manner for local inspections.

Conclusions

The author concludes that:

1. *Ignorance on the part of public officials,* including legislators, at all levels of government of the legitimate purposes and uses of building codes; and incompetent code enforcement, *not the codes themselves, are the problem.*
2. The publication of the "Dwelling Code" sponsored jointly by all of the proprietary model code publishing organizations at the urging of the National Association of Home Builders (NAHB) will prove the truth of conclusion No. 1 above.
3. A Federal Building Code is *unnecessary* and *undesirable* and *would stifle rather than encourage innovation. The publication of such a code would be a national disaster.*
4. *Fifty State Building Codes would be fifty disasters.*
5. The National Institute of Building Sciences could be beneficial to the construction industry in the United States *provided its activities are controlled by an autonomous governing body truly representative of all facets of our society having an interest in building construction.*[38]

[38] See "Who Sustains the Clamor for a Federal Building Code?", p. 56.

The need for an autonomous representative body to control the proposed Institute is illustrated by the following: Any group planning or operating a government program will come in time to be, or feel, expert in that program—to feel that it knows what makes sense with regard to that program and what does not. Thus, it will resent and resist attempts by the organization or by others (Congress for example) to make changes in the program. Furthermore, it is very easy for the group to acquire such self-confidence with regard to the program that it thinks any suggestion that does not originate within itself is unwise. In this way, expertness often breeds inflexibility and resistance to change.[39]

6. *Adoption of one of the four existing nationally recognized model building codes without amendment throughout each metropolitan area including those that cross state boundaries would, for all practical purposes, eliminate the code problems of the construction industry.*

7. *The Department of Housing and Urban Development (HUD) has the tools for bringing this about without any additional legislation or appropriations.*

8. *The Department of Housing and Urban Development (HUD), because of its broad perspectives (as compared with the narrow scientific and engineering interests of the National Bureau of Standards in the Department of Commerce) should be directed by the President and/or the Congress to supervise and coordinate all of the code activities of the Federal Government.*

In this chapter, we have discussed the question of a Federal Building Code and have concluded that such a code is *unnecessary* and *undesirable*. We have indicated that the Department of Housing and Urban Development (HUD) already has the tools needed to bring about almost complete uniformity in building code requirements throughout the nation's metropolitan areas, if not the entire country. Finally, we have suggested that HUD is the logical Federal Department to coordinate all Federal code activities.

In Chapter VII, we shall examine the broad role of HUD and other Federal agencies in our nation's code system.

---

[39] Herbert A. Simon, Donald W. Smithburg, and Victor A. Thompson, *Public Administration* (New York: Alfred A. Knopf, Inc., 1950), p. 117.

The Role of HUD and Other Federal Agencies

THE Department of Housing and Urban Development (HUD), our nation's newest cabinet level department (created by an Act of Congress September 9, 1965) is, as far as the quality of life of our individual citizens is concerned, probably our most important Federal department.

HUD was born, in the opinion of the author, of the desperate plight that faced most of the nation's cities and urban areas because rural dominated state legislatures had failed to recognize the needs of their urban citizens and had failed to enact legislation that would permit local governments to solve their own social and economic problems.

The magnitude of these problems is shown by the following: Today our nation's population is roughly 200 million, with more than 57 people to every one of our $3\frac{1}{2}$ million square miles. Of this number, about 70 per cent, or 140 million, live close by each other in urban areas and densely populated cities on 1 per cent of the nation's total land area. Some statisticians estimate that by the year 2000, this urban population will be about 250 million—two times the present size. The non-urban population, estimated at 75 to 100 million, will live only a short drive or quick plane ride from an urban area. The nation will, in fact, be almost totally urbanized. Even sooner than the year 2000, between now and 1976 (only 200 years after the Declaration of Independence) we will need 2 million new homes a year, schools for 60 million children, health and welfare programs for 27 million people over the age of 60, and transportation facilities for the daily movement of 200 million people in more than 80 million automobiles.

This tremendous growth and the resulting demand for facilities and services is confirmation of the fact that we have entered a new era in our nation's history, the urban era. Another indication of the "urban era" has been the tremendous increase over the past 50 years in the number of local jurisdictions of all types: the 15,000 that existed in 1915 have grown to 90,000 in 1965, an increase of 500 per cent. In spite of this growth, only 20 per cent of all local jurisdictions are located in metropolitan areas. The average number of governmental units for a metropolitan area is 87, but several areas now have over 1,000 local units.

The proliferation of local governmental jurisdictions is greatest in metropolitan areas. Thus, while the total number of these local units decreased in the five years ending in 1962, the number of units in metropolitan areas increased by over 3 per cent. This increase is due largely to the creation of new cities, villages, towns, and special districts in metropolitan areas.

Similar growth trends are evident for governmental employment. While Federal civilian employment will have increased 22 per cent from 1958 to 1968, state and local governments will have increased employment by more than 70 per cent. State and local employment, as a percentage of all government employment, will have increased from 71 per cent in 1958 to an estimated 77 per cent in 1968.[1]

In the United States the administration of the necessary functions of government are shared by Federal, state and local officials. "The American form of government is often, but erroneously, symbolized by a three-layer cake. A far more accurate image is the rainbow or marble cake, characterized by an inseparable mingling of differently colored ingredients".[2]

In law enforcement (including code enforcement) and education, two of the most local of local functions, the state and Federal governments play important roles.

The most obvious examples of shared functions are the Federal grant programs. The grants utilize the greater wealth-gathering abilities of the central government and establish nation-wide standards, yet they are "in aid" of functions carried out under state law,

---

[1] *Vice President's Handbook for Local Officials: A Guide to Federal Assistance for Local Governments* (Washington: U. S. Government Printing Office, 1967), p. 2.

[2] Morton Grodzins, "The Federal System", *The American Political System: Notes and Readings,* eds. Bernard E. Brown and John C. Wahlke (Homewood: The Dorsey Press, 1967), p. 576.

with considerable state and local discretion. *The national super-vision of such programs is largely a process of mutual accommoda-tion. Leading state and local officials, acting through their profes-sional organizations, are in considerable part responsible for the very standards that national officers try to persuade all state and local officers to accept.*[3]

The endorsement by HUD of the nationally recognized model codes, in requiring that local governments adopt codes *equal to* the models for "Workable Program" certification, is a good example of this process.

Creative Federalism

During his term of office, President Lyndon Johnson pop-ularized the expression "Creative Federalism" and made the following statements on the need for Federal, state, and local government cooperation:

> The solution to these problems does not rest on a massive program in Washington, nor can it rely solely on the strained resources of local authority. They require us to create new concepts of coopera-tion—a creative federalism—between the national capitol and the leaders of local communities.—May 22, 1964.
>
> Federal energy is essential. But it is not enough. Only a total working partnership among Federal, State and local governments can succeed. The test of that partnership will be the concern of each public organization, each private institution, and each responsible citizen.—January 10, 1967.
>
> No nation so great as ours can develop the society its people need if the Federal government evades its responsibility. This government has not and will not. But neither can such a nation hope to succeed on the strength of Federal action alone. "We began as a nation of localities. And however changed in character those localities become, however urbanized we grow and however high we build, our destiny as a nation, will be determined there."[4] March 17, 1967.

In the preface to the "Vice President's Handbook for Local Officials," former Vice President Hubert Humphrey said this:

> "Were we directed from Washington when to sow and when to reap, we should soon want bread." Those words of Thomas Jefferson

---

[3] *Ibid.*, p. 577.
[4] *Vice President's Handbook for Local Officials*, p. ii.

are more relevant today than ever before. As the American population passes 200 million and as our society rapidly becomes more
complex, there is more need than ever before for viable, creative
government at the local and state levels. For it is the governments
nearest the people that determine the quality of life for the individual; and it is in those smaller units of government that grassroots
democratic participation is best preserved.

There is no question, however, that state and local governments
need outside support as never before. I know of no city in the
United States today that can do the catching-up it needs to do on
the strength of its own resources alone. The same is true in much of
rural America. The problems that confront us demand the utmost
in commitment and cooperation. Their solution requires a Partnership not only between levels of government but between the public
and private sectors of our economy. The times require a Partnership
of responsibility, a Partnership of resources, a Partnership in planning, and a Partnership in achievement. If every American is going
to have the kind of education, the kind of environment, and the
kind of opportunity he is entitled to in the last third of the 20th
Century, Federal support for local initiative is essential.

The Federal government already provides a considerable
amount of assistance. In 1968, Federal aid to state and local governments is estimated to be 17.4 billion dollars, which represents a
three-fold increase in the last ten years. Today, there are at least
450 Federal programs which aid our cities and localities, and they
are carried out by more than 35 departments and agencies. There
are loans, advances, shared revenues, technical assistance, and grants.
The reason for the great variety of Federal programs is the great
variety of local needs. The aim has been to enable localities to
choose Federal assistance specifically tailored to their requirements.[5]

The American federal system has never been a system of sepa-
rated governmental activities. There has never been a time when it
was possible to put neat labels on discreet "federal," "state," and
"local" functions. Even before the Constitution, a statute of 1785,
reinforced by the Northwest Ordinance of 1787, gave grants-in-land
to the states for public schools. Thus the national government was a
prime force in making possible what is now taken to be the most
local function of all, primary and secondary education. *More important, the nation, before it was fully organized, established by
this action a first principle of American federalism: the national
government would use its superior resources to initiate and support*

---

[5] *Ibid.*

national programs, principally administered by the states and localities.[6]

Although the facts of history indicate that there has been loosely structured sharing of the functions of government in America since prior to the Constitution, Americans traditionally are distrustful of centralized power and place great value on the strength and vitality of local units of government. Even though the Supreme Court has given Congress a relatively free hand since 1937 and the Constitution no longer serves to impede centralized government, *the fact remains that the states existed before the nation and still retain a strong constitutional position that places considerable restraint on centralization.*

There are relatively few limitations on the law-making powers of the states and the geography of the nation establishes them as natural centers of administrative and political strength.

Both former President Johnson and now President Nixon have emphasized the need for strong state and local governments. *The Department of Housing and Urban Development is the key Federal agency for maintaining that strength where it exists, bolstering it where it is waning and restoring it where it has vanished.*

Although HUD was established for the express purpose of grouping the federal activities dealing with urban problems, all of the Federal agencies dealing with these problems are not sheltered by its umbrella. This unfortunate circumstance has prompted President Nixon to establish an "Urban Affairs Council", similar to the "National Security Council", for the purpose of focusing the total Federal effort on urban problems in a more efficient manner.

No Single Agency Has the Answers

In Chapter VI, we discussed the involvement of the Department of Commerce in codes activities in some detail. Another agency that is substantially involved is the Department of Health, Education and Welfare. Although other departments are involved to some degree; HUD, HEW and DOC share the primary involvement.

---

[6] Grodzins, p. 577.

The complicity of this involvement and the problems that it poses for local and state government officials is best illustrated by this excerpt from the "Vice President's Handbook for Local Officials":

Housing and Urban Development

Communities which need to improve their standards for the construction and occupancy of housing and which need to modernize codes for all types of building can draw on a wide variety of Federal resources. The Department of Housing and Urban Development can provide extensive technical and financial assistance as an adjunct to its major aid programs.

The Urban Renewal Rehabilitation and the Code Enforcement programs provide consultation and grants to municipalities and counties to undertake activities that will bring structures up to standard. Property owners may obtain financial assistance from the local agencies for conserving and upgrading homes. Among the basic conditions for eligibility are a Workable Program for Community Improvement and properly enforced codes which meet adequate standards of health, safety and welfare. Code enforcement should be coordinated with programs to improve public facilities. The Federal Housing Administration provides consultation on the significance of local code enforcement to property under mortgage insurance programs. The nearest regional office of HUD can advise local officials on both of the above programs.

Health, Education and Welfare

Public health agencies in many jurisdictions play a key role in developing and enforcing certain elements of building codes (especially for sanitary facilities) and standards for occupancy and use of housing (especially multiple-dwelling units) .

Through the Environmental Sanitation program and related activities, the Public Health Service of the Department of Health, Education, and Welfare provides technical assistance in housing code administration and housing quality approval and training to state agencies and, on an ad hoc basis, to local public agencies. The state health agency, or, alternatively, the nearest HEW regional office, can advise local officials on these resources.

Commerce

Information, consultation, and technical assistance for code development and enforcement is also available from other Federal agencies. The Bureau of Standards, Department of Commerce, encourages the development of building codes and standards to insure that structures and equipment will actually perform as required under all probable operating conditions. The Bureau of Standards works with industry, professional organizations, and state and local agencies in modernizing standards and improving specifications for buildings, materials and equipment as part of its housing code specification activity. Local officials who need help on either technical or specifications problems should communicate with the nearest field office of the Department of Commerce. The nearest regional office of the General Services Administration can also provide advice and information on (1) standards for direct Federal construction and Federal contracts with builders, and (2) the relationship of these standards to enforcement of codes. The programs of the Veterans Administration for 'housing' include ad hoc technical assistance to public agencies and groups of citizens. The nearest regional office of the Veterans Administration can advise local officials on the availability of information and consulting services.[6]

On the singular subject of codes and their enforcement, state and local officials are advised to consult with HUD, HEW, DOC (NBS), GSA,[7] and VA.[8] It is obvious that in this one small area, President Nixon's "Urban Affairs Council" has a monumental task.

In the last chapter, we indicated that HUD already had the tools needed to bring about almost complete uniformity in building code requirements throughout the nation's metropolitan areas, if not the entire country. The National Commission on Urban Problems: Recommendation No. 2 (a) spells it out very bluntly:

Use of Federal influence to curb restrictive building code provisions.
The Commission recommends amendment of congressional authorization for water and sewer and other appropriate facility grants to provide as a condition of eligibility for such grants that building codes in communities receiving such grant assistance shall not be more restrictive than nationally recognized model code standards and subsequently the building code standards to be developed by the National Institute of Building Sciences.[9]

---

[6] *Vice President's Handbook for Local Officials,* pp. 185-186.

[7] General Services Administration.

[8] Veterans Administration.

[9] National Commission on Urban Problems, *Building the American City,* Report of the National Commission on Urban Problems to the Congress and to the President of the United States (Washington: U. S. Government Printing Office, 1968), p. 268.

The "Workable Program for Community Improvement" requirements of HUD can be used for this same purpose now by executive order of either the President or the Secretary of HUD.

To quote former Vice President Humphrey, "There is no question, however, that state and local governments need outside support as never before. I know of no city in the United States today that can do the catching-up it needs to do on the strength of its own resources alone."[10]

The tools and the power, *if not the constitutional authority,* to bring about uniform building code requirements in the United States are in the hands of the President and appointed officials in the executive branch of the Federal government. They were available to President Johnson and Secretary Weaver. They are still available to President Nixon and Secretary Romney.

What we have is a *technical problem* that can only be solved by *political action.* **The question is—should the power of the Federal government be wielded, regardless of the political repercussions, on the theory that the ends justify the means? or;**

Are state and local governments important to the concept of "creative federalism" and; do their uniqueness and individuality contribute to the quality of life in America commensurate with the inefficiency and inconvenience that they cause; or, should they be crushed by their own overgrown, spoiled, and bewildering offspring in the name of industrial expediency?

In this chapter, we have examined the role of HUD and other Federal agencies in our nation's code system. We have concluded that HUD has the tools to create nation-wide uniformity in building code requirements but we have left the political decision as to whether or not those tools should be used up to President Nixon and Secretary Romney.

In Chapter VIII we shall look at the Building Officials' organizations and their contribution as "Professional Societies" in the code enforcement complex of the United States.

---

[10] *Vice President's Handbook for Local Officials,* p. ii.

Building Officials Organizations

IN the first seven chapters we have assembled the pieces of the building code system in the United States. In Chapter I, we established that three of the four nationally recognized model building codes were developed and are published by membership organizations comprised primarily of local government officials charged with the administration and enforcement of building regulations. In Chapter V we found that the model codes were the basis of our nation's code system and that substantial uniformity existed in the substantive requirements of these codes. In this chapter we shall examine the Building Officials' Organizations as *professional societies* of code enforcement officers and as *trade associations* serving the broad interests of the construction industry as they are affected by codes and code enforcement.

The Building Officials Conference of America (BOCA)

The Building Officials Conference of America is a non-profit organization serving that branch of government—state, county or local—which regulates construction through building and related codes. The purpose of the organization is to promote the improvement of building regulations and the administrative organization, techniques and methods of their enforcement by local governments. It seeks to make possible the use by the public of new materials and construction techniques that have been proven safe, and to increase the knowledge and understanding of its members in their proper application.

The program and work of the organization is dedicated to:

- the promotion of public safety against the hazards to life and health incident to the construction and use of buildings;
- the advancement of sound methods of building construction;
- the establishment of requirements for prevention of the incidence and spread of fire;
- the relief of the public and industry from the confusion and uncertainty of conflicting building laws;
- the encouragement, enlightenment, and advancement of building officials;
- the furtherance of civic pride and community well being; and
- the substantial growth of every municipality in America.

The Building Officials Conference of America was organized on May 14, 1915, and was formally incorporated under the laws of the State of Connecticut on March 29, 1938. In June of 1946, major changes were made in the Articles of Association, broadening the scope of the organization. These were approved by the Secretary of the State of Connecticut on June 18, 1946.

The organization pursued a program of mutual aid to its membership, with the main feature of the activity being an annual conference. Although codes and code requirements were the principal basis for discussion, and the possibility of the organization sponsoring a building code was discussed in some of the early meetings, no formal code program was established until 1945.

In that year, as the result of existing conditions, a Basic Code Committee was organized and a formal program initiated to produce a building code. Existing available codes were examined and proposals that they be used were carefully considered, but it was determined that the codes then available did not fill the need as envisioned and the conditions under which they were offered for use were not fully acceptable. This activity resulted in the publication of the *BASIC BUILDING CODE and ABRIDGED BUILDING CODE* in 1950. Activities to maintain these codes and to provide services in connection with them were established in 1951 and 1952.

In 1946, a subsidiary organization known as the Building

Officials Foundation was established. The membership of this organization was principally manufacturers of products used in buildings. This organization was controlled by a Board of Governors consisting of the Executive Committee of the Building Officials Conference of America and an equal number of representatives of members of the Foundation who were elected by the members of the Foundation.

The concept of the Foundation was that it would establish an investment fund which would provide income to underwrite a substantial part of the cost of the proposed technical program. This concept was never realized and the funds invested by industry—something less than $200,000—was spent in the initial code development program. In 1952, the Building Officials Foundation was dissolved by vote of the membership of BOF and BOCA, and its liabilities, assets and responsibilities were transferred directly to the Building Officials Conference of America. The members of BOF were transferred to direct Industry Membership in BOCA.

When the BOF was discontinued, an Advisory Committee was established consisting of representatives of 10 Industry Members, five Association Members, and five Technical Members. The purpose of this committee was to recommend a budget, assist in execution of the BOCA program and promotion of adoption of the codes, promote industry membership, and assist in other activities to prevent preparation of a Federal code. This committee was disbanded by action at the annual meeting in 1956.

In 1945, the BOF established a technical office in New York City which served also as a focal point for some of the BOCA activities. Most of the organization work, however, was continued by the officers as it had been handled in the past. In 1952, with the deactivation of BOF, this became the executive office of BOCA and in July 1953, an executive secretary was employed to replace the technical code coordinator who had formerly managed the office. In 1954, the transfer of organizational activity to the executive office was begun.

Late in 1957, the executive office was moved from New York, New York, to Chicago, Illinois, and direct contact was established with other government service organizations located at the Center of Governmental Affairs Organizations at 1313 East 60th

Street. In July 1962, the office was established in the building at that address.[1]

Building Officials Conference of America, Inc.
1313 East 60th Street
Chicago, Illinois 60637

Principal Services

Publishes and Maintains . . .
— Basic Building Code
— Listing of Approved Fire Resistance Ratings of Assemblies of Construction Materials
— Basic Housing Code
— Basic Fire Prevention Code
— Basic Plumbing Code
— Pamphlet on Construction of One- and Two-Family Dwellings
— Research Approval Reports
— BOCA Building Department Recommendations
— The Building Official (monthly)
— The BOCA Bulletin (twice-monthly newsletter)

Provides . . .
— Maintenance of its codes through system of annual changes
— Plan Examination services
— Interpretations of its codes
— Consultation on code activities
— Administrative studies of local government code enforcement agencies.

International Conference of Building Officials (ICBO)

The International Conference of Building Officials, Inc., organized in 1922, as the Pacific Coast Building Officials Conference, is a non-profit service organization incorporated under the laws of the State of California. Its aims and purposes are as follows:

---

[1] Building Officials Conference of America, Inc., *Statement of Organizational History* (Chicago: Building Officials Conference of America, Inc., 1965), pp. 1-3.

- to investigate and discuss the principles underlying safety in the construction, occupancy, and location of buildings and related structures;
- to develop, recommend, and promote uniform regulations and legislation pertaining to building construction, and to encourage uniformity in zoning practice;
- to develop, maintain, publish, and promote the adoption of the Uniform Building Code and related documents;
- to advise and assist in administration of building laws and ordinances; and
- to do all such other things as are incidental to or desirable for the attainment of the above objectives.

Services of the International Conference of Building Officials cover the entire field of building codes and related research activities, plan checking, building department administration, field inspection, and educational program.

In support of its broad program, the International Conference of Building Officials has a complete publishing program of codes, textbooks, research reports and "Building Standards Monthly," the official Conference magazine.[2]

International Conference of Building Officials
50 South Los Robles
Pasadena, California 91101

Principal Services
_____

Publishes and Maintains . . .
— Uniform Building Code
   Vol. I—Construction
   Vol. II—Mechanical
   Vol. III—Housing
   Vol. IV—Dangerous Buildings
   Vol. V—Signs
   Vol. VI—Dwelling House Construction
   Vol. VII—Short Form
— Uniform Building Code Standards

---

[2] International Conference of Building Officials, *International Conference of Building Officials: Its Operating Structure and Service Facilities* (Pasadena: International Conference of Building Officials, 1964).

— Research Reports for Materials, Products, Methods and Types of Construction
— Building Standards Monthly

Provides . . .

— Maintenance of its codes through system of annual changes
— Plan Examination services
— Interpretation of its codes
— Assistance to local officials.

Southern Building Code Congress (SBCC)

The Southern Building Code Congress is a non-profit and non-political association, founded in 1945. The Congress is composed of, supported and sustained by the active membership of governmental bodies such as cities, towns, counties, and states who "pool" their resources to produce the Southern Standard Building Code and related documents.

The Southern Standard Codes are published as a public service and are designed to serve the smallest towns and largest cities. The Congress is particularly interested in promoting uniform building regulations throughout metropolitan areas. Like the other building officials' organizations, SBCC provides a full range of services for its members.[3]

Southern Building Code Congress
Brown-Marx Building
Birmingham, Alabama 35203

Principal Services
———————

Publishes and Maintains. . .

—Southern Standard Building Code
—Southern Standard Building Code—Plumbing
—Southern Standard Gas Code
—Southern Standard Housing Code
—Approval Reports of Committee on Compliance of Products and/or Assemblies
—Southern Building (monthly)

———————

[3] Southern Building Code Congress, *Southern Building Code Congress: What SBCC Is—* (Birmingham: Southern Building Code Congress, 1968) .

Provides ...

—Maintenance of its codes through system of annual changes
—Interpretation of its codes
—Assistance to local officials through staff contact.

To summarize, the building officials' organizations:

1. Publish model codes and related documents;
2. Provide product approval recommendations;
3. Provide consultation and advisory services;
4. Provide plan examination services;
5. Conduct and/or sponsor educational and training programs; and
6. Conduct annual conferences for the exchange of ideas and updating of code requirements.

Product Approvals

We learned in Chapter IV that the construction industry trade associations are active participants in the code changes activities of the building officials' organizations. Another function of these organizations that is vital to the construction industry is their research and product approval programs. This activity is so important that a handbook, "Building Codes: Product Approvals"[4] has been written on the subject. Although the handbook was prepared for the Plastics Group of the Manufacturing Chemists' Association, it should be in the library of any manufacturer of building materials who wishes to market his products on a nation-wide basis.

Since the model codes are *performance codes* which rely on nationally accepted *standards* for established materials and methods, it was necessary to establish a method whereby proprietary products not expressly covered by the codes or standards may be certified by an authoritative agency as acceptable under the performance requirements of the code. The building officials' organizations, when satisfied that a product is acceptable, issue a recommendation that local governments enforcing their model code accept the product. These recommendations are not binding on the users of the model codes but it is rare that they are not accepted.

---

[4] William Demarest, *Building Codes: Product Approvals* (New Haven: Ludlow-Bookman, 1964).

Although the procedures for product approval vary slightly, they are essentially the same as the following briefs will show:

Building Officials Conference of America

Procedures for New-Product Acceptance

BOCA Research Approvals, although recommendations only are recognized and accepted by many local officials because they are supported by factual reports describing the nature and use of the product and its performance under designated standard tests. The reports are directly referenced to applicable requirements of the BOCA codes. The review of technical data by a central agency in lieu of a multiplicity of code authorities has proved beneficial to industry. It makes possible considerable savings in the cost of marketing building products by eliminating the necessity for manufacturers representatives to call on numerous local officials to secure acceptance of those products.

Preliminary Request

The first step in seeking a Research Approval is submission of a *Preliminary Request,* using a form obtained from BOCA for this purpose. The proponent indicates the provisions of the BOCA Building Codes under which the Approval is sought. (Upon request, the BOCA executive offices will assist in preparing submission.) The request must be accompanied by a complete description of the product, its method of installation, and all data that is offered to substantiate the adequacy of its performance. By this preliminary step, BOCA essentially offers the manufacturer an informal review of his entire submission—at a stage when constructive criticism can still be offered, accepted, and put to good use. BOCA's Structural Bureau will study the *Preliminary Request* and, if it is inadequate to prove the applicant's claim, suggest what further information is needed.

Formal Request

Once it is assured that the data he has assembled for submission is adequate, the applicant is supplied forms on which to make a formal request for approval, referring to the data that accompanied the *Preliminary Request*. This is studied exhaustively and a Structural Bureau Report is drafted. This describes fully the building component (perhaps in several slightly variant forms) and its method(s) of installation. It summarizes the test, or group of tests, reported by the proponent to substantiate each performance characteristic claimed. In each instance, the Structural Bureau's opinion is given on the significance of these test results, in terms of whether the product performed satisfactorily in that respect. This is a thorough report, intended to give the building official as complete as possible a story on the component, including its limitations. The pertinent sections of the BOCA Codes are listed and, finally, a recommendation made to the Research and Approvals Committee, indicating whether or not the product is in complete conformity with the provisions of the codes and suggesting any limitations or restrictions that might accompany an approval.

At this stage, the report is termed *preliminary* and comments upon it may be made by the applicant, as well as by members of BOCA's Research and Approvals Committee. Insofar as these comments are in agreement with the data submitted, the Structural Bureau changes the report and then submits it in final form to the Research and Approvals Committee, accompanied by a recommendation for approval or disapproval of the component and by a statement of the reasons therefor. The committee votes as to approval of this recommendation, and also of the final Structural Bureau Report. The applicant does not meet with the committee nor may he comment further, however, provision is made for further consultation as need be, to clear up any question.

Distribution of Approval

Upon approval of the building component, a copy of the entire Structural Bureau Report is provided to every BOCA *active member* (every building official representing a community that belongs to the Conference) for his use. Still wider distribution is given to a 4″ x 6″ card summarizing the approval as follows: number and date, product classification, applicant, product, performance for which approval was requested, recommended approval, and identification of the product in the field.

BOCA's approval, of course, is a recommendation and does not assure acceptance by local communities. But in actual fact, a manufacturer of an approved product can anticipate close to 100 per cent acceptance among BOCA-member jurisdictions, plus a very substantial assist in his submissions to others.

Product Changes

Changes in the physical properties of the product or deviations from the specifications may nullify an approval unless such changes are submitted for review and specifically approved as modifications of the approval. No specific expiration limit is placed on the approval of a project. In order to verify continued compliance with these conditions, applicants are required to file an affidavit annually, certifying that there has been no change in the product or its recommended use since the approval became effective. If there has been a change in the product, the applicant must submit details of the change for review. A certified copy of the annual affidavit of compliance will be distributed to those to whom the initial approval was issued, showing the updating of the approval. If the product has been changed since the approval was granted, the applicant has the option of requesting reexamination, resulting in a new report, or an addendum to the previous report; unless, in the opinion of the Structural Bureau, the change is of such nature that reexamination and reissue of the report is necessary.

In view of the fact that a Structural Bureau Report may be as brief as three pages or as long as 100, it can be seen that a rigid schedule of fees could not cover all possibilities, nevertheless, the applicant's costs are kept to a minimum. Manufacturers are urged to confer in advance (and in confidence) on building-code implications of future products still in development, identifying the pertinent requirements of the Basic Building Code.

Required Standards and Test Procedures

Material and testing standards and accredited authoritative agencies are listed in the appendices to the BOCA Codes. The Conference does not list testing laboratories whose reports it will recognize exclusively, but merely emphasizes the need for data from qualified sources. If a company provides data from its own laboratories, the tests must have been conducted under the direct observation of a registered professional engineer acceptable to BOCA (or by a BOCA representative). Similarly, the seal of an engineer must appear on calculations, design information, plans, etc., submitted with an application, together with his statement that this work was done under his direct supervision.

International Conference of Building Officials

New-Product Acceptance Procedures

An application for approval (formally called a *Research Recommendation*) is made on a form provided for the purpose, accompanied by a dozen copies of all supporting data. This, together with an analysis and report by the Technical Director on the ICBO staff, is forwarded to the members of the Research Committee for review in advance of a public hearing before the committee. The committee may call for additional testing by an independent laboratory under a program formulated by the Technical Director. The applicant pays for such tests and receives a copy of the laboratory's findings reported to ICBO.

If approval is recommended, it is for a one-year period followed by annual reexaminations. If approval is not recommended, but the application is held for further study, it becomes automatically cancelled after six months (unless the committee votes its continuance).

The fee for original review is sent with the application and is not refunded if the product is not deemed to conform with the objectives of the Uniform Building Code. Each Research Recommendation is transmitted to the entire membership of ICBO by means of 5″ x 8″ cards carrying the essential information. The recommendation generally sets forth the limitations within which the product may be used under the Uniform Building Code. There are fees for each subsequent annual reexamination.

Examination and reexamination fees may cover a number of products if they are identical in nature. When a *Research Recommendation* covers more than one type of product or when the accepted product is to be sold under the names of companies other than the proponent, there are further charges for each additional product or brand-name. In addition, there is an annual charge for listing approved components in ICBO's magazine, "Building Standards Monthly".

Southern Building Code Congress

New-Product Acceptance
Procedures

Application for approval is made upon a form provided for that purpose which is submitted with a deposit, and five copies of substantiating data, i.e.; test reports, product literature, engineering computations, installation instructions or drawings, etc. The submission must include a brief, but complete description of the component and its uses. When a product is particularly unusual, it is advisable to review the entire submission with the SBCC technical staff.

Material submitted is routed to the Structural Bureau of the Congress for analysis and preparation of an approval brief. A copy of the brief and a set of the proponent's supporting data, is sent to each member of the Committee on Compliance. If the committee approves the component as complying with the provisions of the Southern Standard Building Code, the members sign the brief which is then duplicated and sent to all code enforcement agencies holding membership in the Congress.[5]

Benefits to Industry

By providing industry with a means for participating in the development and updating of code requirements and a means of rapidly securing code acceptance of newly developed proprietary products, the building officials' organizations in the United States offer innovators unlimited opportunities. The only restriction placed on innovations under this system is proof of the performance claimed by the innovator.

Educational and Training Programs

Probably the weakest area for all of the building officials'

---

[5]*Ibid.,* pp. 3-9.

organizations is the matter of training and education. While the special interests of industry have substantial financial backing, the training needs of local government code enforcement agencies have had little or none. The expertise in this area is present in the staffs of the building officials' organizations but the limited size of these staffs and the demands made on their time by other organizational responsibilities makes it impossible for them to do much more than provide advice and counsel to state and local educational institutions.

Funds are now available for training code enforcement personnel through several programs of the Federal government, however, a coordinated nation-wide program has never been developed.

All three organizations conduct code "workshops" as part of their annual conferences and BOCA conducts them on the *National Building Code,* published by the American Insurance Association,[6] as well as on the *Basic Building Code.*

The National Coordinating Council

Although the Building Officials Conference of America was established in 1915 as a professional society of building officials, the publication of model building codes, first by the Pacific Coast Building Officials Conference (1927), then by the Southern Building Code Congress (1945), and finally by BOCA itself (1950), served to prevent the formation of one nation-wide organization that would be acceptable to all building officials in the country without regard to the code they used. Nevertheless, the leaders of these three organizations recognized that there was need for coordinated action in some areas of code enforcement. Accordingly, a *National Coordinating Council* was established on May 4, 1957. The purposes of the Council were to:

a. advise and recommend policies and procedures to member groups to promote unanimity of action on a national scale.
b. assist buildings officials to establish themselves and their departments as a professional activity of civic government.

---

[6] The American Insurance Association is not a *Building Officials* organization and does not have building official members Many building officials who use the *National Building Code* are active members of the Building Officials Conference of America.

   c. maintain liaison with Federal government agencies and officials with regard to developments or activities as they apply to the profession.

   d. communicate to the member groups, information on discussions, projects, or activities related to building code and standards work.

   e. coordinate the activities of the member groups to avoid conflicts in scheduling of meetings and conferences.

From 1957 until 1962, the National Coordinating Council (NCC) was an ad hoc arrangement that apparently accomplished little. In 1962, however, it was formally established and conducted regular meetings in conjunction with the annual conferences of the participating organizations.

Probably the most significant achievement of NCC was the adoption in May of 1964 of the following program:

Seven Point Program

1. All segments of the building industry concerned with building codes actively and progressively promote in local communities with which they have contact, the adoption of either the Basic Building Code, Southern Building Code, or Uniform Building Code; recommending that this adoption be without prejudice or local amendment except as may be necessary to adapt the code to the administrative organization, and that all communities in a metropolitan area adopt a similar code.

2. All segments of the building industry actively and progressively support the establishment of enabling legislation where none previously exists, to authorize local governments to adopt building codes by reference without bias of authorship.

3. All segments of the building industry actively and progressively participate in the activities of BOCA, ICBO and SBCC, and standards development, promoting rational regulations of all products based on fact without prejudice.

4. The building industry coordinate and provide a means to accomplish the following goals:

   a. Correlate research development in the industry and provide for dissemination of this information;

    b. Establish recommended standards in clearly defined terms based on the research of information set forth in item a.

    c. Promote the establishment of new standards including good practice procedures where none presently exist.

5. The aid of educational institutions and other organizations should be solicited to provide for the educational or professional upgrading of personnel engaged in administration of building codes.

6. Clear-cut areas of responsibility of state and local agencies for the promulgation and administration of regulations governing buildings be established in order to eliminate over-lap, duplication and conflict between state agencies, and between state and local agencies.

7. A public relations program be established to inform the public of the advantages of modern, minimum performance building codes as stated herein.

Further, that the term *Building Industry* refers to all persons, manufacturers, associations, enforcing agencies or other organizations interested in building regulations, and that the term "Standards" applies to recommended material specifications or test procedures which do not include conditions of acceptance.

The National Board of Fire Underwriters (NBFU),[7] subsequently advised that it would support the program provided the *National Building Code* was included in item 1 and NBFU was included in item 3.

On March 1, 1967, the Council established an office in Washington, D.C., for the purpose of developing an effective liaison between building officials, industry and Federal government agencies.

The benefits anticipated by the participating organizations in establishing a Washington office did not materialize, however, and NCC was dissolved exactly one year later.

Although there is no formal coordination of the activities of the building officials' organizations at this time, they have all become members of the Member Body Council of the American National Standards Institute and are cooperating in the develop-

---

[7] The National Board of Fire Underwriters (NBFU) is now the American Insurance Association (AIA).

ment of a comprehensive set of standards for use in building codes. As mentioned in Chapter VI, they are also cosponsoring a building code for one- and two-family dwellings.

The publication of the *dwelling code* will require the establishment of a permanent body that is representative of all of the building officials' organizations and the American Insurance Association for the purpose of keeping the code up-to-date.

It seems ironic that significant accomplishments are being made through informal arrangements, where formal organizations have failed.

Model Code Standardization Council

In addition to the building officials' organizations, a group known as the Model Code Standardization Council (MCSC) has been working toward code uniformity for twenty years. Formed in 1949 as the Joint Committee on Building Codes (JCBC), this group includes representatives from the National Bureau of Standards, Department of Housing and Urban Development, American National Standards Institute, National Fire Protection Association, American Insurance Association, Underwriters' Laboratories, Inc., American Institute of Architects, American Society of Civil Engineers, National Research Council of Canada, Building Research Advisory Board, National Conference of States on Codes and Standards, and the three building officials' organizations; BOCA, ICBO, and SBCC.

All organizations represented in MCSC are involved either in the development of standards or codes or in code enforcement.

Subjects discussed by MCSC include the latest developments in standards, codes, new products and types of construction. A current project of MCSC is the development of a standard set of definitions and terms used in building codes.

Because of the broad representation on MCSC, it should continue to be a valuable part of the code system in the United States.

In this chapter, we have concluded part one of this book by examining the building officials' organizations as they serve both government and industry. We have observed some successes and some failures.

In part two, we will look at the problems of code enforcement and the administration of building regulations.

PART TWO

Code Administration

Chapter

IX

The Field Is Law Enforcement

THE official called upon to enforce the building laws, whether he is called commissioner, superintendent, inspector or anything else, *is a police officer*; not, of course, in the restricted sense of a person whose business it is to patrol a certain beat for a fixed period of time for the purpose of arresting offenders against the provisions of the criminal laws, but in the broader sense of a guardian of the peace. His immediate concern, however, is to see that the public safety to life and limb is secured by the observance of such laws as it has been found necessary to make with respect to the construction of buildings.

Rudolph P. Miller
First President
Building Officials Conference of America

In Part I of this book, we examined the *code system* that exists in the United States. In this part we will examine the factors involved in the administration of building regulations (code enforcement) and the broader responsibilities of those public officials (building officials) who administer those and other regulations.

The Building Official

A building official is a law enforcement officer; a highly specialized law enforcement officer whose prime mission is the prevention and correction, or abatement of violations. Building code violations, housing code violations, plumbing, electrical, heating, refrigerator and elevator code violations; plus violations of the zoning ordinance, air pollution control ordinance, aban-

101

doned vehicle ordinance, weed ordinance and *any other code or ordinance that the local legislative body is not quite sure what to do with.*

A building official designs nothing, builds nothing, repairs nothing and demolishes nothing. His responsibility is merely to see that those persons who are engaged in these activities do so within the requirements of the law.

The Building Department

The governmental unit that is administered by a *Building Official* is a law enforcement agency (code enforcement) and for that reason its sole mission is, or should be, to enforce those laws, ordinances and regulations that have been assigned to it. In a properly organized local government, this agency will have departmental status and its administrator will report directly to the chief executive of the jurisdiction. It is not unusual, however, to find this vital function buried as a bureau or division in some other department such as public works, public safety, planning, or community development. In St. Paul, Minnesota, it is part of the parks department.

Most building officials are charged directly with their enforcement responsibilities by charter or ordinance *even though they may be subordinate, as a bureau chief or division head, to another official who is not so charged.* Building officials who are constrained by this type of misorganization are in the untenable position of being charged directly by law with enforcement responsibilities, while at the same time having their actions subject to review, revision or even reversal by an official who *does not* have specific law enforcement responsibilities.

Without direct access to their chief executive, they must channel their problems through the *filtering system* of their immediate superior or risk his wrath by going over his head. The first choice deprives the chief executive of direct information that is vital to his overview of community affairs, and the second destroys the trust necessary to a satisfactory superior-subordinate relationship.

The regulations enforced by code enforcement agencies are usually ordinances adopted by local governments under the *police power* that has been delegated to them by the state. In some cases, however, they are state laws that require enforcement by local governments. The *police power* of the states is generally accepted to be their power to legislate for the public health, safety, and general welfare. The United States Supreme Court has said, however, that it (the police power) is "incapable of any very exact definition."[1]

A few states have adopted state-wide building codes but most states have delegated this responsibility to local governments such as cities, counties and townships. When states delegate this responsibility to local governments, the local governments are limited in their authority by a statute which is known as an *enabling act* to the powers that are actually delegated. Enabling legislation may be general and grant broad authority to local governments to enact ordinances concerned with the public health, safety and general welfare or it may be very specific and authorize only the regulation of the construction and maintenance of buildings.

When state regulatory codes and local regulatory codes are in conflict, the state code takes precedence, except that more stringent local regulations do not necessarily conflict.[2] State codes frequently provide specifically for the adoption of local regulations that are more stringent than those of the state.

Local governments may not delegate their police powers. However, they may provide for the administration of their regulatory codes by turning them over to an officer such as a building official, provided there are sufficient standards in the codes to guide him in making decisions as to the conformity of proposed construction to the code.[3]

Such officials do not have unlimited discretion, however, and it is an established principle of law that a legislative body has no constitutional authority to delegate arbitrary discretionary power to administrative officers. Municipal ordinances which authorize public officials to exercise arbitrary discretion without prescribing uniform rules of action or without establishing positive standards

---

[1] Charles S. Rhyne, *Survey of The Law of Building Codes* (Washington: American Institute of Architects, National Association of Home Builders, 1960), p. 6, citing Slaughter House Cases, 83 U.S. (16 Wall.) 36, 62 (1872).
[2] *Ibid.*, p. 7, citing Taggart v. Latah County, 79 Idaho 99, 298 P.2d 979, (1956) King v. Arlington County, 195 Va. 1084, 81 S.E.2d 587 (1954).
[3] Rhyne, p. 7.

for the control of the officials is void, unconstitutional and outside the powers of a municipality.

Generally the courts have held that regulatory ordinances must establish uniform rules and may not depend on the arbitrary will of local government authorities. One exception to the general rule is that ordinances do not always need to prescribe specific rules of action because some situations require that some discretion be given to local government officials when it is difficult or impractical to establish definite rules for guidance, or when the discretion is related to the administration of police regulations and is essential to the protection of the public health, safety or general welfare. Matters of discretion as to details of enforcing ordinances that are valid otherwise may be left to designated officials.[4]

A municipal ordinance prohibiting building without a permit but authorizing the building inspector to grant such a permit if satisfied that the proposed building complied with the requirements of the ordinance was held unconstitutional as conferring an absolute and uncontrolled discretion on the building inspector, since it made no provision as to what should be deemed necessary to constitute a safe construction . . . *The test in respect to whether or not the conferring of discretion to refuse an application for a permit is valid is whether the applicant can determine beforehand from the contents of the statute or ordinance all the necessary requirements therefore.*[5]

Tests for Ordinances

Before adopting any regulatory ordinance, local legislative bodies should assure themselves that it meets at least these three tests:

1. *Necessity.* Is it necessary to protect the public morals, health, safety, or general welfare?
2. *Reasonableness.* Is it reasonable, by virtue of being fair, general, impartial, and not in conflict with the common rights of individuals nor, unduly oppressive to them?
3. *Enforceability.* Can it be efficiently enforced under the limitations of: the remedies available under civil law; and/

---

[4] Rhyne, p. 15.
[5] Rhyne, p. 16.

or, the sanctions of criminal law; and/or, the capabilities of enforcement personnel?

Regulatory ordinances which do not meet these three tests are bound to prove troublesome at some stage of the enforcement process.

The strong predisposition in this country to believe that any behavior can be controlled by threatening punishment has filled American statute books with hundreds of unenforced and unenforceable laws. In the final analysis, the chief inducement force of legal sanctions is social—the desire to avoid the social stigma of being publicly branded a law breaker.[6]

Since a large segment of our society today lives in relative anonymity in congested areas of major cities, there is little deterrent value to the incarceration sanction because little or no social stigma attaches to an anonymous law breaker.

Inspection

While law enforcement in our modern society is commonly associated with the suppression of crime, the police and the courts are far from having exclusive responsibility for the enforcement of the ever increasing social regulations that are essential to the morals, health, safety and general welfare of an urban society. The regulatory functions of government that are designed to control the use of private property in the broad public interest have increased with great rapidity in the past few years. The sociological problems of urban America have created a steadily increasing dependence on governmental regulatory agencies.

It is a relatively simple matter to adopt regulatory laws, but their value depends on the judgement, efficiency, impartiality and continuity with which they are administered. Unfortunately, a large segment of the American public still retains a naive belief that our legal system is automatically self-enforcing. This belief is a holdover from the early period in the development of the modern state when the function of complaint was left to private citizens who were expected to file complaints against those who violated the law. Although the complaint function gradually

---

[6]Herbert A. Simon, Donald W. Smithburg, and Victor A. Thompson, *Public Administration* (New York: Alfred A. Knopf, Inc., 1950), p. 479.

became the specialized duty of the police, the older practice of the duty of the individual to report violations of the law still remains. Until very recent times, government relied heavily on aggrieved citizens to bring action against violators of the law and today there is a resurgence of citizen complaints, especially in the ghettos of our major cities.

As social regulations became more complex, the complaint process became more specialized and today the police are no longer the primary complaint agents. The police still work with the criminal law and other matters such as traffic regulation and the keeping of the peace, but the discovery and reporting of violations of technical regulations is increasingly being entrusted to *inspector specialists*. These *specialist police officers* are the building, housing, plumbing, electrical, fire and many other inspectors who enforce the codes and ordinances that are too technical for the general police officer to enforce effectively. It is a general function of inspectors to seek out violations.

> Writers on administration frequently distinguish administrative regulation from judicial regulation by saying the former is preventive while the latter is corrective or retributive. The chief difference, however, is that the administrative agencies actively seek out violations that would never be reported under judicial regulation with its reliance on the regular police and the public prosecutors. As a consequence, administrative regulation achieves more compliance because it engages in more enforcement—t has a more highly organized complaint system.[7]

The effectiveness of a code enforcement agency is dependent essentially on its inspection processes. For lasting effect and community improvement, inspections must be made of both new construction and periodically of existing buildings. The procedures involved in these two types of inspections are necessarily different since the one involves the actual construction process and the other, the maintenance and occupancy of a completed building. The details of both types of inspections will be discussed in Chapters XIV and XV.

A consideration that properly belongs in this chapter is that the inspection of existing buildings involves entry of private residences without a warrant. Such inspections are subject to pos-

---

[7] *Ibid.,* p. 481.

sible objection as unreasonable searches and a deprivation of due process of law within the meaning of the Fourteenth Amendment to the United States Constitution. Many state constitutions also have similar provisions.

The Fourteenth Amendment and state constitutions notwithstanding, code enforcement officers had little interference from the courts until June of 1967, when the United States Supreme Court held, in the case of Camara v. Municipal Court (San Francisco), that..."the citizen may lawfully refuse to admit the housing inspector in a non-emergency situation, where such inspector is not possessed of a search warrant or probable cause to believe the local housing ordinance is being violated."[8]

The foregoing may lead the reader to conclude that the ruling of the United States Supreme Court in the Camara case has presented code enforcement officers with a serious handicap to their enforcement procedures. It is my belief, however, that the importance of the case has been blown up out of all proportion to its impact. In my sixteen years with the Detroit Building Department, I knew of only one entry refusal and that was overcome by a more diplomatic inspector. After discussing this question with code enforcement officials from all over the country, from both large and small cities, I conclude that securing entry to occupied buildings for the purpose of making legitimate regulatory inspections is not a problem of any magnitude.

The Rules of Administrative Law

The rules of administrative law describe what protection the courts will give to individuals against administrative action that violates the social rules of enforcement ...

By far the most important bulwark of the social rules of enforcement is the reaction of the public to highhanded inducement methods. Violation of the accepted rules of enforcement simply leads to less compliance and is therefore self-defeating ...

Enforcement activities cannot be a monopoly of attorneys if excessive legalism is to be avoided. To secure compliance, the public relations or educational activity must be kept coordinated with all other activities and especially with planning.[9]

---

[8] David F. Polatsek, "'Who Goes There'—The Right of Entry and Housing Code Enforcement", *Journal of Urban Law* XLVI, 2 (1969), p. 279.
[9] Simon, Smithburg and Thompson, pp. 483-487.

If the field is law enforcement—and it is, and the building official is a police officer—and he is, then what are the tools of his trade? And what qualifications does he need in order to perform the duties of his office?

Whatever his background, the Building Official must learn his profession on the job, because the knowledge he brings with him can be little more than a base for what he has to learn. What he must have are those skills that are required in any top-level administrator.

If the administrator is not a subject matter specialist, then what are his particular skills? A partial answer is that they are the skills of organizing and managing complex groups of men and skills of negotiating and of representing these groups in their relations with other groups. Such skills are obviously required in any organization, and a person who has successfully exercised them in one should be able to do the same in another.[10]

In this chapter, we have established the administration of building regulations as part of the broad field of law enforcement. In Chapter X, we will examine the problems involved in the administration of a code enforcement agency.

---

[10] *Ibid.*, pp. 349-350.

The Chief Executive
and the Legislature

EVERYTHING in this book that precedes this chapter and everything that follows, is subordinate. This chapter is the reason this book had to be written.

Inept administration is the essence of the ills of code enforcement in the United States. Only a recognition on the part of local government chief executives and legislators that the principles of good public administration must be applied to code enforcement and the administration of building regulations will bring about any noticeable improvement in the situation.

No administrative organization in this country can come into being or long exist without the support of the legislature and usually the chief executive. The legislature provides the legal authority and the funds for the organization. The legal basis of the organization includes not only the definition of its goal or objective, but very often also a rather detailed description of the organizational structure. The legislative body also passes many laws that stipulate how the organization may carry out its objective—laws relating to the management of personnel, accounting for funds, expenditures, procurement, the rights of the citizen as against the organization, and many others . . .

In some cases the chief executive has various kinds of legal authority, either in his own right under the Constitution or by delegation from the legislature, that he may redelegate to an administrative organization. Given this legal framework, it is clear that an administrative organization must have the support of the legislature or the executive—and usually both—if it is to come into existence and continue to exist.[1]

---

[1] Herbert A. Simon, Donald W. Smithburg, and Victor A. Thompson, *Public Administration* (New York: Alfred A. Knopf, Inc., 1950), p. 383.

In this chapter I shall dogmatically declare the criteria for an *effective* and *efficient* code enforcement agency and the principles on which it must be operated. My dogmatism is prompted by my experience, however, I shall call upon the writings of those considered experts in the field of administration for support of my precepts.

As my first supporter, I call upon Chester I. Barnard, probably the most quoted American author in the field of administration, and his discussion of the distinctions in the meanings of the words *effective* and *efficient*. Rewriting his statement would either distort or dilute it, so I quote:

> When a specific desired end is attained we shall say that the action is *effective*. When the unsought consequences of the action are more important than the attainment of the desired end and are dissatisfactory, effective action, we shall say, is *inefficient*. When the unsought consequences are unimportant or trivial, the action is *efficient*. Moreover, it sometimes happens that the end sought is not attained, but the unsought consequences satisfy desires or motives not the *cause* of the action. We shall then regard such action as *efficient* but not *effective*. In retrospect the action in this case is justified not by the results sought, but by those not sought. These observations are matters of common personal experience.
>
> Accordingly we shall say that an action is *effective* if it accomplishes its specific objective aim. We shall also say it is *efficient* if it satisfies the motives of that aim, whether it is *effective* or not, and the process does not create offsetting dissatisfactions. We shall say that an action is *inefficient* if the motives are not satisfied, or offsetting dissatisfactions are incurred, even if it is *effective*.[2]

A properly organized and managed code enforcement agency can and should be both *effective* and *efficient*.

Criteria for Successful Code Enforcement

1. All code enforcement functions must be in one agency.
2. Code enforcement must be the sole function of the agency.
3. The code enforcement agency must have department status.
4. The administrator of code enforcement must be responsible directly and exclusively to the chief executive.

---

[2] Chester I. Barnard, *The Functions of The Executive* (Cambridge: Harvard University Press, 1968), pp. 19-20.

Department Status

The central idea of public administration is rational action, defined as action correctly calculated to realize given desired goals. Public administration both as a study and as an activity is intended to maximize the realization of goals.[3]

An administrative system is distinguished both by the authoritative and personal interrelations of its organizational structure, and the management actions intended to achieve rational cooperation. One of the reasons that certain activities are grouped together is to insure that proper emphasis will be placed on those aspects of a program that are considered most important. A single purpose department has an organizational independence that places great emphasis on its sole function. On the other hand, if a relatively small unit is placed in an organization where its contribution is considered to be unimportant or even troublesome and a hindrance to the rest of the organization (which is often the case of code enforcement agencies that are bureaus or divisions of *catch all* departments) , it may become a *stepchild* and be neglected or even scorned and ridiculed by the top executives and other members of the organization.

When an organization has a wide range of activities, attention will usually be centered on those that have the most glamour and the others will be considered as sidelines worthy of little attention. A half century of code criticism and the physical decay of our central cities appears to be ample evidence that code enforcement, as an activity of local government, warrants more than a *stepchild* status.

Sole Function—Code Enforcement

The goal of a code enforcement agency is *code enforcement* and nothing else. The goal of municipal government might be the attainment of an ideal urban community, but the goals of the component agencies of that government must, of necessity, if they are to meet Barnard's concepts of *effective* and *efficient,* be relatively narrow. It is the responsibility of the legislative body to provide the chief executive with the authority to organize for the implementation of their legislative mandates, and it is the respon-

---

[3] Dwight Waldo, *The Study of Public Administration* (New York: Random House, 1955) , p. 11.

sibility of the chief executive to utilize every resource at his command to carry out those mandates. It is the function of the chief executive to reconcile the narrow goals of the component agencies in order to attain the broader goals of municipal government as a whole. To quote Barnard again, "It is precisely the function of the executive to facilitate the synthesis in concrete action of contradictory forces, to reconcile conflicting forces, instincts, interests, conditions, positions, and ideals.[4]

Direct Responsibility to the Chief Executive

Far too many local government chief executives fail to function as executives for a multitude of reasons. It is my feeling that in many cases their failure to act stems from a lack of knowledge of the breadth of their authority and/or an apprehensiveness of treading on the hallowed playground of some entrenched local bureaucrat.[5] Unfortunately, failure to act for the latter reason may be prudent when the power setting of a bureau[6] is such that its administrator actually has a considerable degree of autonomy.

The external environment of any bureau depends greatly on the particular society and era in which it exists. Hence any analysis of bureau behavior must take into account prevailing social conditions, including the level of relevant technologies.

However, not all portions of a bureau's external environment are equally relevant to its behavior. The bureau is responsible for certain social functions that provide benefits and costs for persons outside of itself. The persons and agencies affected by the bureau and their relationships to it form its power setting in the external environment.[7]

One of the greatest power resources of a bureau is its *clientele group*. These are the *customers* of the bureau and their satis-

---

[4] Barnard, p. 21.

[5] As used here, the term "bureaucrat" means an administrator who is not elected to his office and is not dependent for his tenure on the election or re-election of his nominal superior.

[6] The term "bureau" is used here in the broad context and applies equally to other designations for operational units such as "department", "division", or "section".

[7] Anthony Downs, *Inside Bureaucracy* (Boston: Little, Brown and Company, 1966), p. 44.

faction or dissatisfaction with its administration contributes greatly to the health and status of any bureau. Some *clientele groups* are so powerful that their support, through their influence on the legislature, can insure the survival of an organization or whose opposition can bring about its demise or at least substantial modification of its goals and methods of operation. A well organized *clientele group* may have such an impact that it will be called upon to *clear* legislation affecting its interests. "Those who are regulated must generally approve of, or at least accede to, these programs. Administrative regulations can not be enforced against a generally hostile public."[8]

Public opinion may have some influence on a particular agency but there are many *publics* and those groups most vitally affected by an agency's activities usually have little difficulty in establishing their group as the authoritative voice of *the people*. Nevertheless, a genuine public hostility toward the program of an agency would probably bring about the abolition or at least substantial revision of that program.

The survival of effective regulation, like the survival of any governmental activity, requires a positive balance of political support over political opposition. The necessary political support may be forthcoming from any of three sources (not necessarily mutually exclusive) :

1. Support may be provided by large or politically powerful segments of the community that are not included in the agency clientele and whose interests are in some respect opposed to those of the clientele . . .

2. Governmental regulations may actually advance, rather than oppose, the interests of politically powerful segments of the clientele group . . . Professional licensing laws have been increasingly used to protect the economic and status positions of established members of the professions by limiting entrance to the professions . . .

3. A clientele group may accept regulations even though somewhat adverse to its short-run interests as a means of anticipating and heading-off potential political forces that would otherwise impose more severe and less palatable regulations upon the group . . .

In any case, where regulation exists, interest groups in the

---

[8] Simon, Smithburg and Thompson, p. 385.

clientele will have strong reasons to try to influence or control the regulatory process.[9]

An administrator of a regulatory agency may be highly satisfactory to his *clientele group* and, if he is skilled in the art of public relations, build his personal image to a point where he is considered almost *untouchable.* At the same time, the performance of his agency may be completely unsatisfactory to the chief executive and not at all in keeping with the goals established by the legislature. This is a situation that could be considered *efficient* but not *effective* within Barnard's meaning because the unsought consequences satisfy desires and motives without attaining the end sought.

It is also a situation that usually results from the failure of the administrator to recognize the changes in the exterior forces that effect the goals of his agency. In many cases, administrators of code enforcement agencies have continued to cater to their *clientele groups* (builders, contractors, property managers) while the positive balance of political power shifted to new *activist* citizens' organizations such as *block clubs* and *tenant unions.* **They have sat on the comfortable corners of their responsibilities playing with their slide rules while their politically responsible (elected) superiors took the *heat* of the *people* problems created by their myopic inadequacies.** Meanwhile their *clients* have fled to the suburbs, taking their votes and their businesses with them. While the *clients* still make forays into the city, their political *clout* is limited to campaign contributions (which may be substantial) and moral support. As a defeated mayor of Detroit discovered, the back slapping and well wishes of such supporters, even when backed up by campaign contributions, may not be enough on election day.

In most of our older cities, both large and small, the emphasis is on maintenance, conservation, rehabilitation and renewal, yet, many code enforcement agencies have failed to shift gears to accommodate the changed emphasis. More than a few mayors and city managers have discovered that their code enforcement administrators were incapable of adjusting to the new emphasis.

When a chief executive is faced with this situation and is unable to redirect the agency's efforts toward its official goals,

---

[9] *Ibid.,* pp. 462-463.

he has no alternative but to replace the administrator. Such an action calls for a high degree of intestinal fortitude, however, if he keeps in mind that the *power* is in the office, not the individual; and that the *clientele group* still has to deal with the agency, he should be reassured.

Actually, he may find that the replaced administrator's image was a myth and that the *clientele group* is grateful to him for ridding them of a despot.

In many cases, a chief executive is unable to replace the code enforcement administrator because his job is protected by *civil service* regulations. However, many solutions to this problem have been devised. The two most frequently used are the creation of a *super* department (which this writer does not favor because of the communications problems mentioned earlier) and the reorganization of the existing department in a manner that will downgrade the position of the unsatisfactory administrator who has job tenure but will permit the appointment of a new department administrator responsible directly to and removable by the chief executive.

Resourceful chief executives have used these and other means to supplant an ineffective code administrator.

The technicalities of effecting such reorganization are as variable as state laws and city charters but there are few legal obstacles that cannot be overcome by the cooperative efforts of the chief executive, legal counsel and the legislature.

The Clientele Group

A code enforcement agency deals with a *clientele group* that has interests that are frequently at odds with the best interests of the public at large, nevertheless, some of the regulations that are enforced by the agency may actually advance, rather than hinder the interests of the *clientele group*. Although the licensing of contractors and tradesmen such as plumbers and electricians is ostensibly to protect the public, *it is actually used in many cases by the tradesmen and unions who control the licensing boards to limit entry into the trades and maintain an artificial and unnecessary shortage of tradesmen*. When such regulations prohibit property owners from doing their own work, even when they are capable of doing it, and when the code enforcement agency is responsible for seeing that it is done properly, one questions the true purpose of the regulations.

When the avowed goal of a code enforcement agency is the protection of the public health, safety and general welfare through enforcement of building regulations, a major part of its efforts are or should be directed toward preventing or securing correction of the mis-deeds or mistakes of its *clientele group*.

Under its dual role of protector of the public, and protector of the tradesmen, it is easy to see why the agency's performance can be highly satisfactory to its *clientele group* and very unsatisfactory to the city fathers at the same time.

As the balance of political power tips more and more toward the vociferous urban *activists,* it should be obvious that the chief executive *must* have unfiltered information from his code enforcement administrator and *must* be accessible to him.

One Code Enforcement Agency

One of the biggest headaches to people dealing with local government code enforcement agencies and perhaps the biggest obstacle to effective code enforcement is the fact that there is no one agency that handles all code enforcement. In most cases there isn't even a central *information agency* that could direct someone to all of the agencies involved in some aspect of code enforcement.

It is not at all unusual for a building to be completed and its owner issued a *certificate of occupancy* by the building department and then be ordered by the fire marshal to install costly and unsightly sprinkler systems, fire alarms, exit signs, fire escapes, stair enclosures, etc., or by the health department to install additional or different sanitary facilities and special equipment.

Even if he has managed to comply with all of the local requirements, his building might be found in violation by an inspector from some state agency that had not been taken into consideration. The number of agencies involved is a small part of the problem, however, in comparison to the number of violation notices issued by these *after the fact* or *latter day* inspectors, who, in many cases have no legal basis for their orders, but make up the rules as they go along.

In some buildings in the central cities, slum area multi-family dwellings in particular, there is such a continuous parade of inspectors that the occupants hardly acknowledge their presence. While working on housing inspections in Detroit, I was frequently escorted by caretakers through apartments while the occupants were in bed. Sometimes they covered up, and sometimes they didn't, but they never seemed surprised or resentful of the intrusion on their privacy.

The best way to present the enforcement problems created by several agencies working without coordination in the same general area is to cite a hypothetical case that is based on similar cases that actually happened.

A person bought a large old one-family dwelling in a block that was zoned for one-family dwellings and decided to convert it to four small apartments. The two story building had four bedrooms and one bath on the second floor and a living room, parlor, dining room, kitchen and pantry on the first floor. There was one stairway to the second floor. Without even inquiring about permits, the new owner installed two kitchen sinks and two gas stoves on the second floor which he then rented as two- two room apartments. He also installed another kitchen sink and gas stove on the first floor which he also rented as two- two room apartments. He was now renting what was legally a one-family dwelling as four apartments all sharing the same bath and with only one means of egress from the second floor. At this point, an inspector from the fire marshal's office made an inspection and observed that there were four apartments in the building but only one means of egress. The state multi-family dwelling law required two means of egress when there were three or more apartments in a building. He ordered the owner to provide a second means of egress from the second floor. The owner complied immediately by building an outside fire escape. Next, an inspector from the health department made an inspection and observed that there was only one bathroom for four- two room apartments and ordered the owner to install one additional bathroom to meet the minimum requirement of the state multi-family dwelling law of one bathroom for each two apartments. The owner complied immediately by installing the bath fixtures in the first floor pantry. Finally, an inspection was made by a building inspector who observed that the building was occupied as four- two room apartments, had two means of egress from the second floor and one bathroom for each two apartments as required by the state multi-family dwelling law. However, when he returned to the office and checked the records he found that the building was located in a one-family dwelling zoning district, that it had been built thirty years ago under a permit issued for the construction of a one-family dwelling and that no subsequent permits had been issued. He sent the following notice to the owner:

1. Vacate and desist in the use of this building as four apartments and restore to its legal occupancy as a one-family dwelling only.
2. Disconnect and remove the three kitchen sinks and first floor bathroom fixtures that were installed without a plumbing permit.
3. Disconnect and remove the three gas stoves that were installed without a permit.
4. Dismantle and remove the fire escape that was installed without a permit.

The owner failed to comply and a complaint was filed by the building inspector in municipal court. When the case was heard, the owner produced the notices that he had received from the fire department and health department as evidence that he had only acted to comply with the orders he had received from the city to comply with the state law. The judge found him not guilty and criticized the city because its code enforcement agencies did not coordinate their activities. *Through incompetent code administration, an undesirable substandard occupancy had become established and the deterioration of a single family residential neighborhood had begun.*

Situations similar to, but even more ridiculous than, the one above have happened and are still happening throughout the United States today. *It doesn't have to be that way.*

Those local government chief executives who have the *courage to perform as executives* and ". . . facilitate the synthesis in concrete action of contradictory forces, to reconcile conflicting forces, instincts, interests, conditions, positions, and ideals. . ."[10] have merely to look at the city charter for their guidelines on a course of action. Many might be surprised to find that they can

---

[10] Barnard, p. 21.

solve their code enforcement coordination problems merely by issuing executive orders for reorganization. It is more likely, however, that assistance from the legislative body will be needed and in some cases, charter revision. Whatever the technicalities, some toes will be stepped on because at least three departments are involved; buildings, fire and health.

In this chapter, we have involved the chief executive and the legislature in the administration of building regulations. In Chapter XI, we shall examine the basis for organization of a code enforcement agency.

Organizing For Code Enforcement

IN order to organize for effective and efficient code enforcement, it is first necessary to establish that the *goal* of the agency is *code enforcement*. The emphasis here is on the singular *goal* of *code enforcement* as modified by Barnard's concept of the meaning of the words *effective* and *efficient*. "When a specific desired end is attained, we shall say that this action is *effective*... When the unsought consequences are unimportant or trivial, the action is *efficient*."[1]

A code enforcement agency might be *effective* in terms of securing compliance but be *inefficient* because the unsought consequences of its actions are dissatisfactory and more important than compliance. The methods used by a code enforcement agency and the attitude of its personnel can cause unsought consequences that are highly unsatisfactory to the administration.

By far, the most important bulwark of the social rules of enforcement is the reaction of the public to highhanded inducement methods. Violation of the accepted rules of enforcement, simply leads to less compliance and is therefore self-defeating.

The difficulty of administering an unpopular program makes administrators tend to seek popular ones, and failure to achieve a popular program is probably more often a result of administrative ineptitude than of administrative viciousness. For this reason, probably the greatest hope for individual protection, for liberal administration, lies in the education of administrators rather than the introduction of outworn judicial procedures in administration.[2]

---

[1]Chester J. Barnard, *The Functions of The Executive* (Cambridge: Harvard University Press, 1968), p. 19.
[2]Herbert A. Simon, Donald W. Smithburg, and Victor A. Thompson, *Public Administration* (New York: Alfred A. Knopf, Inc., 1950), p. 486.

Code Enforcement Activities

Having established that the *goal* of the agency is *code enforcement,* it then must be determined what functions and activities are necessary to achieve the goal and what methodology is best suited to each activity.

We can start by asking and answering the question: What does a typical code enforcement agency do in attempting to achieve its *goal?*

- *It examines and licenses*—plumbers, electricians, air conditioning and refrigeration contractors, television repairmen, boiler operators, wrecking and house moving contractors, welders, sign erectors and steeplejacks.
- *It issues permits*—for buildings, structures, signs, alterations, demolition, plumbing, wiring, refrigeration and heating equipment, and use of land.
- *It inspects*—all new construction, alterations, land uses, and all equipment for which permits are issued; and the amusement riding devices in carnivals and amusement parks; and the tents at circuses and revival meetings.
- *It periodically inspects*—places of public assembly, hotels, night clubs, hospitals, rooming houses, factories, stores, multi-family dwellings, schools, churches, and jails.
- *It issues violation notices*—to builders, contractors, property managers, tenants and home owners.
- *It conducts show-cause hearings*—to give violators an opportunity to arrange for compliance.
- *It enters complaints in court*—when compliance cannot be secured.

Examination and Inspection

In summary, achievement of the *goal* of *code enforcement* involves two basic functions which each generate several activities. The two basic functions are *examination* and *inspection.*

The *examination* function is distinguished from the *inspection* function in that it occurs *before the fact* and its purpose is to *predetermine* the possibility of compliance. The *inspection* function, on the other hand, occurs *after the fact* and its purpose is to *determine* if compliance has been achieved, and if it has not, to take the action necessary to its achievement.

122

The examination function includes both the examination of people to determine their qualifications for license and the examination of proposal documents (plans and/or application) required to determine the conformity of the proposal to applicable regulations.

The inspection function includes not only the inspections that are necessary to secure initial compliance, but those necessary to assure continuing compliance.

The activities generated by the examination function are:
1. Devising and administering examinations.
2. Devising and examining applications.
3. Examining plans.
4. Issuing licenses.
5. Issuing permits.
6. Collecting fees.
7. Keeping records.

The activities generated by the inspection functions are:
1. Inspecting construction (including alterations) as it progresses.
2. Inspecting new equipment as it is installed.
3. Inspecting new land uses as they are initiated.
4. Inspecting existing buildings, structures and land uses periodically.
5. Inspecting equipment periodically for which a permit was required initially.
6. Investigating complaints of violations.
7. Writing inspection reports.
8. Issuing field violation notices.
9. Issuing legal notices of violation.
10. Conferring with *clients.*
11. Conducting *show-cause* hearings.
12. Filing court complaints and appearing in court.
13. Keeping records.

Obviously these activities could be broken down to the specific actions taken by each employee in the agency, however, such minutiae of detail is unnecessary for our purpose.

Personnel Skills

In carrying out its several activities, the code enforcement

123

agency must be so organized as to insure maximum utilization of the skills of its personnel. The skills needed are:

1. Administrative.
2. Professional (lawyers and engineers; civil, mechanical, electrical, sanitary).
3. Technical (inspectors; building, heating, refrigeration, electrical, plumbing, etc.).
4. Stenographic.
5. Clerical.

In order to properly administer a code enforcement agency, *the administrator should be conversant with the professions and trades involved.* When professional or technical people are placed in the role of administrator, *they should be schooled in the principles of administration.*

Line Personnel

Chartism is dear to the hearts of many administrators and there is a certain amount of security in seeing everyone tucked neatly into his own little box with all connection lines leading eventually to the top. We are not going to draw any boxes here, however, we are going to list in rank order the *line* personnel required for a comprehensive code enforcement agency. For this purpose, only those positions having a police type responsibility are considered *line.*

- Chief Executive (Mayor, City Manager, etc.)
- Code Enforcement Administrator (all code enforcement activities)
- Bureau Chiefs (all specialties including fire prevention and sanitation)
- Supervisors (in both the examining and inspection functions)
- Inspectors (including those assigned to office activities)

We have listed the *line* personnel of a code enforcement agency in rank order to indicate that *even in the largest city, there are only three filter points in the communications chain between the inspector in the field and the chief executive.* If he is *accessible,* he should be well informed.

Staff Personnel

All of the other agency personnel are considered *staff* in the narrow sense that their role is to provide the specialized support required by the *line* personnel in the achievement of its *goal*.

Staff services in the broader sense are provided to the code enforcement agency by *outside* departments (other city agencies such as the accounting department, personnel department, purchasing department and corporation counsel's[3] office).

An area critical to effective code enforcement is an understanding on the part of the chief executive, the code enforcement administrator, and the corporation counsel that the corporation counsel's office is a *staff* function that exists solely for the purpose of providing legal services to the operating departments. Unless the chief executive understands this and conveys his understanding loud and clear to both the corporation counsel and the code enforcement administrator, the code enforcement agency has little chance of being *effective*.

Code enforcement agencies in large cities should have their own legal staffs, not only to assist them with court complaints but also in the preparation and revision of codes and ordinances. In smaller jurisdictions, one member of the legal staff should be made exclusively responsible for serving the code enforcement agency.

The subject of legal services is too important to drop at this point without mentioning the *priority problems* that face the typically overburdened corporation counsel. First, he is legal advisor to the chief executive; second, he is legal advisor to the legislative body; third, he is prosecuting attorney and general counsel for the police department; and finally, he is the same for the code enforcement agencies. It is only natural that his top priority assignment is in recognition of the power of the chief executive and the legislature; the next, the glamour and publicity of the police department; and that the code enforcement agencies, with their earthy, unglamourous, relatively picayune, and frequently unpopular regulations, are at the bottom of the list.

---

[3] The term "corporation counsel" as used here means the head of the legal department. City attorney, city solicitor and many other titles are also commonly used.

125

Even if a code enforcement administrator is cognizant of the proper relationship between his agency and the corporation counsel's office, he may be unable to secure the services he needs because his status level in the formal or informal hierarchy of government is less than that of the corporation counsel. To further complicate the problem, the chief executive has frequent need for consultation with the corporation counsel and is, therefore, readily accessible to him. On the other hand, the code enforcement administrator is rarely called upon, except to answer complaints about the operation of his agency, and he finds the chief executive relatively inaccessible. *If the code enforcement administrator is not a department head and does not have authority to contact the chief executive directly, his situation is impossible.*

In the final analysis, the chief executive *is* the chief code enforcement officer. The ultimate responsibility for *effective* and *efficient* code enforcement rests squarely on his shoulders. It behooves him to keep the channels of communication open and to provide the code enforcement agency with the legal services that it requires. Former President, Harry Truman, had a sign on his desk that read, "The Buck stops here." Local government chief executives should recognize that they are indulging in *self-criticism* when they are critical of code enforcement in their own jurisdiction. Only the chief executive can ". . . facilitate the synthesis in concrete action of contradictory forces, . . . reconcile conflicting forces, instincts, interests, conditions, positions, and ideals."[4]

In this chapter, we have examined the basis for the organization of a code enforcement agency and have placed responsibility for that organization, its *effectiveness* and its *efficiency* on the shoulders of the chief executive. In Chapter XII, we shall delve into the question of the personal qualities needed by the individuals who fill the various positions in the agency.

---

[4] Barnard, p. 21.

Chapter
XII

Personal Qualities

W E started Chapter X by saying that its subject matter was the reason this book had to be written and that everything that preceded or followed was subordinate. If we placed all of the other chapters in rank order according to their importance, this one would head the list.

Our objective in this chapter is to make possible substantial improvement in the administration of building regulations in the United States by dispelling two *myths* about the qualifications needed by code enforcement officers.

Myth number one.—The top administrator of a code enforcement agency, whether his title be commissioner, director, chief or any one of a host of others, must be an *architect* or an *engineer*.

Myth number two.—Inspectors should be *journeymen* in one of the building trades.

The professional societies of *architects* and *engineers* and the *building trades unions* have done a masterful job of *taking care of their own* by promoting the adoption of state laws that require that only state licensed or registered *architects, engineers* or *tradesmen* be allowed to fill specified code enforcement positions. *Local governments constrained in their personnel selection by such statutes are unnecessarily carrying a vested interest millstone around their necks that may make effective code enforcement virtually impossible at worst and extremely difficult at best.*

In order to qualify the above, it is necessary and desirable that we repeat some of the observations that were made in previous chapters. First, a code enforcement officer, regardless of whether he is an inspector in the field or the head of the department, is a police officer. Second, a code enforcement officer designs nothing, builds nothing, repairs nothing and demolishes nothing. His prime responsibility is to enforce the regulations over which he has jurisdiction. He will never, *as part of his code enforcement responsibility*, be called upon to use a saw, a trowel, or a "T" square. He does not have to be able to *personally* perform the tasks of the tradesmen in order to determine the conformity of their products to applicable regulations. *In fact, a high degree of skill and many years of experience in the use of any of these tools may, coupled with an ingrained allegiance to the trade or profession using them, prove to be an unrecognized but severe handicap to the development of the skills required of a code enforcement officer.* It is not unusual for persons entering the field of code enforcement after becoming too old to *work with the tools*, or an *unsuccessful career* as an *architect* or *engineer*, to continue to identify with their previous profession or trade and never accept their role as a code enforcement officer as *an entirely different profession requiring knowledge and skills that their pre-entry education, training and experience had not provided them.*

This is an example, in the field of code enforcement, of Thorstien Veblen's concept of "trained incapacity."[1]

Local governments have contributed to their own code enforcement problems by unwittingly placing the best interests of the professional societies and trades unions ahead of that of the general public. It is common practice to unnecessarily and unrealistically restrict certain positions to persons holding specific academic degrees and/or professional licenses or registrations *even though the duties of the position may never call upon the knowledge or skills required to secure these documents of academic or professional recognition.*

While lesser animals stake out territorial claims man lays claim, not only to physical property, but also, to those occupations that he considers his own special province. He limits even *peripheral* activities to members of his own tribe whom he identifies by providing them with *symbolic credentials* such as membership cards, licenses, registrations, certificates and diplomas.

It is not at all unusual for a local government to require

---

[1] Robert K. Merton, "Bureaucratic Structure and Personality", *A Sociological Reader on Complex Organizations*, ed. Amitai Etzioni (New York: Holt, Rinehart and Winston, Inc., 1969) , p. 50.

that code enforcement inspectors belong to a building trades union. *The latter is about as logical as requiring that a police officer be a card carrying member of the mafia.* The conflict of interest in this situation is so obvious that it should never be tolerated.

Trade union practices are a veritable coral reef of accumulated defenses against extreme emphasis upon individual performance. One of the leading authorities on labor once said, "The good Lord made more slow workers than fast workers. Don't ask me why. The fast workers can look after themselves under any system, it is the business of the trade union to look after the slow ones." This is by no means the only task of the union, but the statement is correct.[2]

Many of the problems of staffing a code enforcement agency are shared in common with other agencies and it is appropriate at this time that we quote Harold Howe II, former U.S. Commissioner of Education.

Changing the Pecking Order

The Barnyard Hierarchy which chickens establish among themselves is a natural phenomenon that we all take for granted. We call it "the pecking order." It brings the larger, the stronger, or the more confident chickens to the feeding trough before the skinny, introverted ones, who most need to be fed. But in the hierarchy of social and occupational dominance, prestige and authority based on academic or titular credentials are human phenomena that I am afraid we cannot afford to take for granted. It is our somewhat artificial human pecking order that requires some examination.

It seems to me extremely important to the survival and the health of America that we find ways for the institutions which control opportunity in our society to do so with a concern for those people who have been denied opportunity by the shortcomings of the society.

It is of desperate importance in a viable and open social system that we learn to cherish and nurture a variety of talents with adequate appreciation for each. Former Secretary of Health, Education, and Welfare John Gardner pinpointed this neatly for us when he wrote:

"An excellent plumber is infinitely more admirable than an incompetent philosopher. The society which scorns excellence in

---

[2] John W. Gardner, *Excellence: Can We Be Equal and Excellent Too?* (New York: Harper & Row, 1961), p. 111.

plumbing because plumbing is a humble activity and tolerates shoddiness in philosophy because it is an exalted activity will have neither good plumbing nor good philosophy. Neither its pipes nor its theories will hold water."

I'd like to go a step further and suggest that it is not inconceivable that our excellent plumber might also have the makings of an admirable philosopher. We have no accurate way of knowing that he would not. If we think he would not (and we probably do), it is most likely because he has no degree in philosophy.

Which may be a bit like saying that Socrates wasn't a good teacher because he had no teaching credential—and suggests that we have forgotten that Spinoza earned his living as a lens grinder and that Tom Edison quit school at the age of nine.

My point is that an academic degree or a diploma is a fairly good indicator of ability—but only in a negative sense; in the sense that a person who has such a degree or diploma is probably not intellectually inadequate.

But taking the symbol for the substance is not the hallmark of good and careful judgment or of attention to individual differences. We should never automatically assume that the person with some letters after his name will perform better than the person without those letters. We should never automatically assume that the person who has held a job precisely like one we are trying to fill will perform better than the person who has no comparable experience.

Unfortunately, people are individuals, and institutions deal in multitudes. There is never time to inspect each person, to grade him like a cut of beef, and stamp him prime, choice or good. Administrative necessity dictates the establishment of some criteria on which to base selection.

There is considerable evidence that public policy and institutional practice make it extremely difficult for competent but un-credentialled persons to have a fair crack at competitive situations, whether they be social, vocational, or educational.

Without question we need broad minimum standards in a whole basketful of categories. And we need efficient ways to determine whether or not our applicants meet those standards. But efficiency cannot be our only criterion. No matter what system we use to evaluate people, we need to build in provisions for unique individuals and reasonable allowance for not-so-unique individuals who have some special attribute.

I don't think we are terribly good at this.

At almost every level, in almost all fields, we find an automatic emphasis on credentials, a routine rigidity, whether the credential

130

under consideration is a high school diploma, a Ph.D., or a certificate from a beauty college . . .

This credentialling myopia is by no means confined to the disadvantaged. In almost every occupation, at almost every level, one finds certification requirements of one kind or another locking people out of situations in which they might well be substantial contributors. This remains true, though we know that new technology changes job functions so fast that adaptability may be more essential in a prospective employee than any specific knowledge or specific training . . .

Until we learn how to tell when people are competent, we will continue to have a great many people going to school for the wrong reasons and a great many more who are not going to school for the wrong reasons. As managers and as admissions officers we are going to lose a lot of "mute, inglorious Miltons" unless we find some better ways to measure potential ability and unless we can serve larger numbers of people with an education which helps the individual reach the credential rather than failing him because he can not reach it in the same fashion as others . . .

There is a paradox here: We've committed ourselves to the credentialling system, and now we need to find ways to beat it. The institutions which are involved in it must now learn to act on behalf of the people who are affected by it . . .

All our carefully developed forms of exclusion might make economic (if not moral) sense if society was oversupplied with skilled manpower. At a time when we face desperate shortages in almost all professions and skilled trades, it is wasteful and dangerous . . .

Those who are already established in a profession or occupation are usually responsible for maintaining its standards. When a credentialling review committee is established, somehow its members always come up with tougher entrance requirements. Rarely does anyone ever suggest making it easier to get in and the possibility of getting some good people that way.

It is human nature to want to keep our club hard to get into; logic always loses when the ego is threatened . . .

These are not frivolous matters. When we determine the educational and vocational limits of individual lives by such practices, procedures, and symbols, we not only do injustice to the individual but we inflict a potential talent loss of inestimable consequence to the Nation.

What can we do about it? We certainly cannot do away with credentials—they are as much a part of the contemporary scene as taxes and television.

But we can minimize their impact of a negative kind by having the wisdom to use them wisely and flexibly. We can, as I said earlier, develop some new ways to acquire them . . . We can do this; we can break down the professional roll so that subprofessional jobs open up. More importantly we can relate the sub-professional role to the professional so that a person can shift from one to the other with greater ease . . .

We must remember that some people will learn whether or not they have the advantage of college experience; that some other people, if they have staying power, can end up with degrees that really don't mean much.

We can continue to search for better ways to evaluate people, more sophisticated ways to measure ability, skill, and potential. And finally, we can build escape clauses into all our certifying, credentialling, and admissions procedures to allow individual consideration or people with special situations, unique talents, or measurable handicaps.

None of this is enough to change radically the pecking order, but if we are conscientious in our effort to look at people, not paper, and offer honest second chances educationally and professionally, we may be able to help a few skinny chickens get a little closer to the feeding trough.[3]

There are plenty of young men who are not *tradesmen, architects* or *engineers* who are perfectly capable of becoming excellent code enforcement officers either as inspectors or administrators if we provided training programs for them and could persuade the professional establishment to accept their abilities despite the absence of what are commonly considered (often erroneously) to be the necessary credentials.

A code enforcement officer, be he administrator or inspector, must learn his profession on the job. The knowledge or skills that he brings with him from a trade or some other profession can be little more than a base for what he has to learn.

The Inspector

The many facets of *communication* are far more important in code enforcement than in the trades or the design professions. To be effective, an inspector must have some exceptional abilities

---

[3] Harold Howe II, "Changing the Pecking Order", *Civil Service Journal,* IX, 1 (July–September, 1968) , pp. 12-16.

that warrant special mention. None of them involve the use of tools other than a pencil.

They are:

1. Observation
   a. of documents
   b. of field situations
2. Comprehension
   a. evaluation
   b. interpretation
3. Narration
   a. verbal
   b. written
4. Instruction
   a. verbal
   b. written

In the preceding chapter, we established the two basic functions of code enforcement as examination and inspection. What, then, are the *powers* and *skills* of man that are called upon by the processes involved in code enforcement?

Observation

The first is the power of *observation*. He must be able to see. Whether he is in a field situation involving actual construction or in an office examining plans, he must see and see well.

Comprehension

Seeing, in itself however, is valueless as far as code enforcement is concerned without *comprehension*. He must *comprehend* what he sees in order to be able to *evaluate* what he *observes* and *interpret his observations* in light of his responsibilities as a law enforcement officer. This means that he must be able to *read*, not just with *minimal* understanding, but with a *very high degree of comprehension*. Digesting the technical requirements found in regulatory ordinances does not come easy for many *attorneys, architects* and *engineers* and we cannot expect more from people whose literary tastes are limited to comic books and the sports pages. In addition to being able to read and interpret codes and ordinances, inspectors must also be able to *read* working drawings or *blue prints* and understand the symbols employed in their details.

Narration

The ability to *comprehend* both *documents* and *situations* merely brings us to the point of beginning in securing the correction or abatement of a violation of a building regulation.

Having *observed* that a situation is in violation of some regulation, what must be done? If it is a minor problem that can be easily corrected, as is often the case with violations occurring during the course of construction, and the foreman or tradesman is on the site, it may only be necessary to verbally instruct him in order to secure compliance. In most cases, however, (in every case where the correction cannot be made before the inspector leaves the site) it is necessary that the facts of the situation be recorded. *An inspector must be able to write a concise report, not just as an aid to his own future recall of the situation, but in sufficient detail to clearly depict the situation to anyone reading the report even though they had never personally visited the site.* His supervisor or any other inspector should be able to reinspect the site, using his report with complete confidence that they know exactly what he had observed to be wrong. An inspector who cannot write concise narrative reports is not only useless as a code enforcement officer, he is a liability to his agency.

Instruction

Coupled with his ability to write concise narrative reports, *an inspector must be able to formulate and effectively issue understandable instructions.* A person who is responsible for the correction of a violation must know exactly what he must do in order to comply. In the case of the minor construction violations that are handled verbally, clarity alone is not sufficient. The manner in which instructions are issued verbally can be as effective, either positively or negatively, as the instructions themselves.

Notices of violation issued by code enforcement officers are not the same as violation *tickets* issued by traffic policemen. Their purpose is not to cite the violator and order him into court for violating an ordinance, but to instruct him in what he must do to correct or abate the violation. *A violation notice issued by a code enforcement officer is actually a correction notice wherein the violator is given specific instructions as to what he must do to comply.*

An inspector, then, must be able to formulate and issue clear instructions both verbal and oral in a positive but inoffensive manner.

The reasons for dividing the writing skills required of an inspector into "narration" and "instruction" will be explained in detail in Chapter XIV.

Personal Qualities

The ability to *observe, comprehend, narrate* and *instruct* are *basic skills* that *must be required* of all code enforcement inspectors but there are also personality traits and factors of moral character that are equally important.

Code enforcement inspectors have more direct personal contact with a greater cross-section and volume of people than any other group of municipal employees. Every working day they are in contact with the public in homes, factories, schools, hotels and stores. It is not unusual for an inspector to meet with architects, engineers, lawyers, clergymen, millionaire businessmen and destitute welfare clients all in the course of a day's work. In many cases, he is a citizen's only contact with local government and personifies *The City* to that individual.

In addition to the *public contact* aspect of his job, the code enforcement inspector has the same freedom of movement as an outside salesman, *but without the incentive of a potential commission to encourage him to make one more call.* It is practically impossible for a supervisor of inspectors to evaluate their productivity unless he has been one himself, and even then it is difficult.

In summary, the personal qualities required of a code enforcement inspector are:

1. *Self-respect*—he must think well of himself if he is to evoke the respect of others.
2. *Pleasant personality*—he must be a basically happy person with a tolerant understanding of human nature.
3. *Neat personal appearance*—he must be well groomed and dress in a manner appropriate to his assignment.
4. *Integrity*—he must be impeccably honest, not just from the

standpoint of code enforcement but in devoting full time during his working day to his duties. To steal time from one's employer is as reprehensible as stealing his property.

5. *Motivation*—he must enthusiastically believe in and support the goal of his agency and he must believe that his personal role is essential to the achievement of that goal.

The Administrator

If the skills and personal qualities listed above are essential for an inspector, what are those necessary for the Code Enforcement Administrator? Certainly, they would include all of those required of inspectors (we haven't discussed specialized technical knowledge) plus those that are required of any top level administrator. They are the skills of organizing and managing complex groups of men and of reconciling contradictory or conflicting forces, instincts, interests, conditions, positions, and ideals.

Paranoia

Some observers, and particularly the critics of bureaucracy, have hypothesized that positions in public administration attract individuals whose personal needs produce in them "authoritarian" tendencies. By authoritarianism, we mean the love of power over others, whether or not it is accompanied by a philosophy rationalizing it.

A love of power may derive from either sadistic or paranoic tendencies. . .

Paranoic tendencies may be present in individuals who enjoy the feeling that high governmental position gives them power over whole industries or a whole nation. Paranoic individuals who are failures in private employment may later seek importance and prestige in government careers.[4]

Since local governments have traditionally hired mid-career or beyond *tradesmen, architects,* and *engineers* as code enforcement inspectors and administrators, it should not be surprising

---

[4] Herbert A. Simon, Donald W. Smithburg, and Victor A. Thompson, *Public Administration* (New York: Alfred A. Knopf, Inc., 1950), p. 545.

that they have attracted some individuals having paranoic tendencies.

Avoiding Personnel Problems

There are time tested and proven testing methods available that can help eliminate many of the pitfalls of haphazard personnel selection. Code enforcement as a vital function of local government cannot be entrusted to persons who are not equipped either technically or emotionally to cope with its problems.

While there will always be a need for technical know-how in code enforcement, effectiveness and efficiency can only be achieved through the skills of administration. It behooves local governments to use all appropriate testing methods in selecting code enforcement personnel and it behooves them to reevaluate the emphasis that is placed on engineering and craftsmanship.

In this chapter, we have looked at the essential qualifications of code enforcement inspectors and administrators. In Chapter XIII, we shall discuss the office procedures employed by a code enforcement agency.

Office Operations

I N this chapter we shall take a broad look at the code enforcement office. What are some of its peculiarities and special problems? Who are its *customers*? Who works there and what do they
do? What are its routine operations? Finally, what is its permanent
contribution to the social and economic stability of the community?

The Customer

Who has business to transact with a code enforcement agency?
There are only two basic reasons for persons to visit the office of a
code enforcement agency. One is to obtain a license or a permit
and the other is to discuss a violation of a regulation enforced by
the agency. All persons, then, who have business with the agency
are seeking something. Even those whose purpose is to complain
about the alleged mis-deeds of others are seeking relief from what
they perceive to be illegal situations.

All *customers* of a code enforcement agency regardless of
whether they are architects, engineers, contractors, wealthy specu-
lators, slum landlords, slum tenants, or private home owners, are
seekers. They want something, either permission to engage in an
occupation or perform a specific act, or relief from a requirement
or situation. This sets the tone of the *customer-employee* relationship in a code enforcement agency. If the *customer* is promptly and
courteously granted that which he seeks, he is a happy and satisfied *customer*. If on the other hand, as is frequently the case, the
agency has no legal authority to grant that which is sought, the
customer will be unhappy and will generally blame the agency or

139

more likely, the individual employee he is dealing with for his frustration. The importance of a sound *customer* relations policy under these conditions cannot be over-emphasized.

The Employee

Whereas the customers in a retail store only come in contact with a counter clerk, those of a code enforcement agency are confronted by a whole chain of employees and may even eventually find themselves in conference with the head of the department. The first contact with the agency may be completely involuntary and the result of an unintentional infraction of some regulation that he was not familiar with.

Who works in the code enforcement office and what kind of people are the *customers* likely to be in contact with? This varies according to the size of the jurisdiction but by considering a comprehensive agency, such as those found in major cities, we can cover them all.

In addition to the counter clerks and cashiers, there are plan examiners who check the plans and applications submitted as evidence of the conformity of proposals to applicable ordinances. Plan examiners are usually engineers or technicians having specialized knowledge in particular subject areas. The larger the agency, the greater the number of specialty examiners. In smaller agencies, field inspectors double as plan examiners and in very small agencies, one man may handle everything.

Field inspectors spend part of each day in the office to file their reports and consult with their supervisors. They are also available during this time for *customer* consultation and may be called upon to explain the details of a situation to their immediate supervisor or, on occasion, to the head of the department.

The Violator

Although there is much ado on the part of those involved in code writing legislation (without practical experience in the realities of code enforcement) about formal appeals procedures, the fact is that there are as many levels of appeal in a code enforcement agency as there are ranks in the hierarchy of the local government. The "Buck" does not stop even at the chief executive

140

level however, since the formal appeal procedures can then be invoked.

Let us trace the path of a substantial citizen with good political connections who has received a violation notice that could cost him several thousand dollars and the income from the property involved is not sufficient to cover the costs of compliance. First, he makes an appointment with the inspector to discuss alternative solutions to the problem. Failing to find one that is acceptable, he arranges to meet with the inspector and his supervisor. Although the supervisor is sympathetic, he feels that the violation is justified and that to waive the requirement would be exceeding his authority, so he asks the chief inspector to consider the problem. The chief inspector is also sympathetic, but suggests that the commissioner be consulted. If relief is not granted by the commissioner and the *customer* has access to the mayor, he may carry his appeal to him before resorting to the formal appeals procedure.

One might ask why a *customer* with access to the mayor would even bother discussing his problems with minor officials such as inspectors, supervisors, bureau chiefs or even the commissioner. The answer can be found in the following:

> The official charged with the administration and enforcement of the building regulations has a great responsibility and with responsibility must go authority. No matter how detailed the building code may be, he must to some extent exercise his own judgement in deciding compliance with the code.[1]

Code enforcement officers, from field inspectors to the chief executive, can only *allege* that in their judgement a violation exists. Only the court can determine that an *alleged* violation is a violation *in fact*. The informal appeal starts with the bottom link in the code enforcement chain of authority because each official must make a determination that might be favorable to the *customer*. If he starts at the top (as some neophytes have learned to their dismay) and is turned down, there is nowhere to go for relief but to a formal appeals board or the courts, either or both of which are often time consuming and expensive.

Another reason for starting at the bottom is that sophisticated supporters of elected officials do not exploit their *political pull*

---

[1] Charles S. Rhyne, *Survey of the Law of Building Codes* (Washington: American Institute of Architects, National Association of Home Builders, 1960), p. 61.

and place their *champions* in compromising situations unnecessarily. Their *in* is used only as a last resort.

Since the violation notice in the first instance is written by the field inspector *based on his observations and knowledge of the law as he understands and interprets it,* it should be obvious that persons of low intellect should not be employed as inspectors. *It should also be obvious that the greater the intellectual gap between the inspector and his superiors, the greater will be the need for review and modification or reversal of his decisions.*

The example cited above was not intended to indicate an improper exercise of administrative discretion, but rather to point out that administrative relief is available within a code enforcement agency. Inspectors do make mistakes, they are sometimes arbitrary in their decisions and issue violation notices that are unwarranted. At any level of supervision, their decisions may be overruled with complete justification. *Citizens should not be herded into court on the whim of an inspector without having an opportunity to be heard by his superior.*

The Permit Seeker

Permits must be secured from a code enforcement agency for everything from the installation of a gas light in a front yard to complete building complexes. In order to show the scope of what this involves, we will use a large shopping center as an example. Without discounting the importance of the preliminary work that has been done by the developer and city officials and agencies, we shall begin when the architect walks into the building department with his working drawings to apply for a permit.

His first stop is an information desk manned by a clerk who provides him with the proper application and directs him to his next stop after he has filled out the application. He then takes the completed application and the working drawings to a permit clerk who examines the application to determine that it is properly filled out and where the plans should be routed, and issues a numbered receipt to the architect, attaches a routing slip to the drawings and files a plan record so that the progress of the application can be traced. The architect is now free to leave and he will be notified by mail when his plans are ready.

Because of the complexity of a major shopping center, every

local government agency that has code enforcement responsibilities and every agency that will be *affected* by its construction must examine the plans. Only those agencies having code enforcement responsibilities can require changes in the plans (within the limitations of applicable ordinances), however, agencies having operations that will be affected by the proposed construction must be alerted so that they can plan their own programs. Also, they may *suggest* changes to the developer that would be in the best interest of the city.

Some, but not all, of the areas that require special knowledge on the part of plan examiners are as follows: zoning, housing, exits, structural design, fire protection, fire prevention, elevators, escalators, heating equipment, refrigeration equipment, pressure vessels, air pollution, plumbing, electrical, sanitation, traffic.

Our shopping center plans will now be routed to the following specialist plan examiners:

1. Zoning
2. Structural Engineering
3. Fire Marshal
4. Safety Engineer
5. Plumbing
6. Electrical
7. Air Pollution Control
8. Sanitarian
9. Traffic Engineer

After the plans have been examined by all of the specialists, they are returned to the permit clerk who notifies the applicant that his plans are ready. If everything was in order, his application and plans would have been approved and signed by each of the specialist plan examiners and the permit clerk can type his permit and send him to the cashier, who upon payment of the prescribed fee, would issue him a receipt and validate the permit. Actual construction could now begin.

It would be quite unusual in processing the plans for something as complex as our hypothetical shopping center, however, if everything was found to be in order. When a plan examiner cannot approve the plans because of nonconformity to an applicable code or ordinance, he attaches a "correction sheet" to the application, setting forth the changes that must be made for

143

compliance and citing the applicable code or ordinance section numbers as his authority. The plan examiner signs the correction sheet so that the applicant can contact him for discussion if he desires. After the applicant has revised his plans to conform to all applicable requirements and has secured approval of the plans as revised, he returns the plans and application to the permit clerk, who types the permit.

The Importance of Plan Examination

Efficient plan examination, coupled with accurate permanent records, is the key to effective code enforcement. The purpose of plan examination is to permit the predetermination on the part of a code enforcement agency, that any proposed construction, alteration, installation or use will upon completion meet the requirements of all applicable codes and ordinances.

Permits cannot legally be issued by a code enforcement agency that are in violation of a code or ordinance within its jurisdiction or under the jurisdiction of some other agency.

Effective plan examination, necessitates the use of comprehensive properly designed permit application forms and insistence that plans and specifications submitted as supporting data with the application be in sufficient detail to insure that the purpose of plan examination is accomplished.

Permit Controls

Building Permits

Proper control of the issuance of building permits is essential to enforcement of the building code, housing code and zoning ordinance.

In addition to the technical aspects of proposed construction, three essential facts must be established:

1. That the applicant for a permit is the owner of the real property involved, or his authorized agent.
2. That satisfactory evidence of ownership has been presented to the permit issuing agency.
3. That the property legally described in the document presented as evidence of ownership corresponds in every detail with that described in the permit application and on the site plan.

144

Conditional Permits

Many building and use permits can only be issued on approval of the Zoning Board of Appeals or, the Planning Commission and/or City Council. These special approvals usually impose conditions not specifically required by ordinance but that are considered necessary by the authoritative body to meet the intent of the ordinance. *They are the strings attached by the authority in exchange for the special concession that has been granted to the applicant.* They are an integral part of the agreement between the authoritative body and the applicant.

It is essential for initial and continuing compliance that these conditions be an integral part of the permit and permanent records.

Permits should not be issued unless a copy of the special approval is attached to the permit application and when the permit is issued, a copy of the special approval should be attached to the inspector's field copy of the permit.

Permits should not be completed nor certificates of occupancy issued until all special conditions have been fulfilled.

Mechanical Permits

Proper control of the issuance of mechanical permits substantially reduces illegal changes in the uses and occupancies of buildings. Mechanical permits, especially plumbing and electrical permits, should not be issued unless the city can determine that the proposed work will not contribute to such a change. The tools used to make a determination are properly designed application forms, reference to open building permits, reference to department records, and, if necessary, an inspection of the property in question.

Without proper control of the issuance of mechanical permits, the landlord in our hypothetical example of an illegal occupancy change in Chapter X might have been able to present a plumbing permit to the court that was issued by the same department that entered the court complaint.

Code enforcement agencies that have been *burned* by such experiences usually establish a *clearance* procedure that requires a record check and approval by the building division prior to issuance of mechanical permits.

145

Processing the Plans

Let us look now in some detail at what was actually involved in processing the plans and application for our hypothetical shopping center from the time they were left with the permit clerk until the architect was notified that they were ready to be picked up.

After the routing slip has been attached to the plans and specifications by the permit clerk they are placed in a routing bin and begin their journey by messenger from one specialist plan examiner to another until they are returned to the permit clerk.

Zoning

The first examination is made by a zoning specialist who checks the legal description on the application against the site plan and the site plan against the zoning map to determine what zoning district the property is located in. After determining that the legal description is accurate and the proposed general use is permitted in the zoning district, he begins a systematic analysis of the proposed construction in light of the requirements prescribed by the zoning ordinance for that specific occupancy in that specific zoning district.

Some of the specific requirements that have to be determined are:

1. The permissibility of each individual business proposed to occupy the sub-units of the complex.
2. Location of the buildings in relation to the property lines.
3. Size and location of signs.
4. Size and location of service areas, loading docks, etc.
5. Off-street parking facilities. (This is no small task in the case of a shopping center when zoning ordinances typically have different requirements for each occupancy.) Not only the number of spaces but also the size of each space, the parking angle and the aisle width must be determined.
6. Special requirements imposed by the Planning Commission or the Zoning Board of Appeals such as special facing materials for certain building elevations, ornamental fences and walls, or even the size and species of trees and shrubs to be planted in *green belt* areas.

Thoroughness on the part of the zoning plan examiner is essential if the intent of the zoning ordinance is to be secured. There is no specific academic training that prepares people for this role, however good reading comprehension and sound logic are *musts*.

Housing

Housing is not normally a consideration in a shopping center, but in order to cover all plan examination interest areas, we will list those items that the housing plan examiner is concerned with. They are:

1. Occupancies.
2. Room sizes and arrangements.
3. Light and ventilation (including open spaces such as yards and courts).
4. Sanitary facilities.
5. Supplied facilities (heat, hot water, screens, etc.).
   Housing plan examiners should have the same abilities as zoning plan examiners.

Structural Engineering

Plans are checked by the structural plan examiner for four basic reasons:

1. To determine that the calculations used in the design of the structural members of the building are accurate and meet the requirements of the building code.
2. To determine that the use of fire resistant materials as protection for the structural members and as components in wall and floor-ceiling assemblies meets the requirements of the building code.
3. To determine if the exit facilities meet the requirements of the building code.
4. To determine if the special protections required by the building code because of the inherent hazards of certain uses or occupancies have been provided for.

It should be obvious that the first determination can only be made by a *structural engineer* and most major cities in the United States require that a structural plan examiner be a *registered pro-*

fessional engineer. Small jurisdictions, either retain consulting engineers or just don't bother checking the engineering calculations and hope that the designer's calculations are correct. The latter course is a dangerous one and the question of the city's liability in case of structural failure, even when the designer is a registered architect or engineer, has yet to be decided by the courts.

Local governments that adopt the Basic Building Code published by the Building Officials Conference of America may have their plans checked for a nominal fee by the professional engineering staff of that organization.

The other three areas usually investigated by the structural plan examiner *do not* call upon special engineering knowledge, and since determination of conformity can be made by the use of simple mathematics and a comparison of the code specifications with the design specifications, this work can be done by non-engineering personnel who have good reading comprehension and training in *blue print* reading.

Schools of architecture and engineering have traditionally devoted little, if any, class time to code requirements and it is unrealistic to expect their graduates to have sufficient knowledge of them to design with infallibility. Even though most state registration laws require that professional architects and engineers comply with all applicable laws in their designs, they are limited in their ability to comply by their *unintentional but nonetheless limited* knowledge of code requirements. In addition, many code requirements impose design limitations that the designer would prefer not to know about. It is the responsibility of the code enforcement agency to enforce the law even when dealing with licensed *professionals* who have pledged faithful compliance in order to secure their license.

The *professional*, whatever his calling, is still a human being and no lofty code of ethics can separate him from the temptations and weaknesses of humanity. Prison gates throughout our country have opened in cynical welcome to those who have misused their *professional* license. It is irrational, if not illegal, to delegate enforcement responsibility to the individual being regulated.

Plumbing

Plans are checked by a plumbing specialist to insure compliance with the plumbing code. In major cities, he may be a sanitary engineer, but it is more likely that he will be a senior plumbing inspector assigned to that responsibility by the chief plumbing inspector who is, in most cases, a professional engineer.

Plumbing codes are *specification codes* and it is the task of the plan examiner to compare the design specifications with the code specifications. Some plumbing codes such as the Basic Plumbing Code published by the Building Officials Conference of America, are in sufficient detail to be used as design manuals.

The prime purposes of all plumbing regulation are two-fold:

1. To bring potable water into a building and to distribute it to the point of use without contamination and without danger of contamination to the exterior source of supply, and

2. To convey liquid-borne sanitary wastes out of a building and into a sewage disposal system that has been accepted by the appropriate government jurisdiction. (The pollution of the waterways of America with raw or inadequately treated sewage and the fouling of millions of acres of land by malfunctioning septic tank systems precludes the use of such terms as *approved* since many communities accept the use of inadequate systems even though they do not approve of them.)

Plumbing code requirements that go beyond the two prime purposes are incidental but may be of almost equal importance.

Some of the basic items checked by the plumbing plan examiner are:

1. Pipe sizes and materials used for waste and supply lines.
2. Venting systems.
3. Vacuum breaking devices.
4. Number, type and spacing of fixtures.
5. Floor and wall surfacing materials used in rooms containing plumbing fixtures.
6. Light and ventilation of rooms containing plumbing fixtures.
7. Special equipment required by occupancies having unusual disposal problems such as slaughter houses, food processing plants, restaurants, medical clinics, hospitals and mortuaries.

149

There are many others (every occupancy has its own special requirements) however the above list will serve to point out the scope of interest of the plumbing plan examiner.

Electrical

Plans are checked by an electrical specialist to insure compliance with the electrical code. He may be an electrical engineer, but it is more likely that he will be a senior electrical inspector assigned to office duties as a plan examiner.

The prime purposes of electrical regulations are to prevent fires due to overloaded electrical circuits and to prevent loss of life due to contact with energized or "hot" wires or other conductors of electricity. It is no accident that the National Electrical Code is published by the National Fire Protection Association or that Underwriters' Laboratories, Incorporated, originally sponsored by the National Board of Fire Underwriters is internationally recognized as the ultimate authority in the determination of the adequacy of both the design and quality of the materials and equipment used in electrical power and lighting systems.

The electrical code, like the plumbing code, is a *specification code* and it is the task of the plan examiner to compare the design specifications with the code specifications. His analysis begins with a determination of the occupancy of the building and the amount and kind of equipment that it will contain. With this basic information, he can compute the potential "load" that may be placed on the power supply and determine the size of the service required.

Some of the basic items checked by the electrical plan examiner are:

1. Number and distribution of convenience outlets.
2. Size of conductors and methods of grounding.
3. Location and types of switches.
4. Size and location of service and service entrance cable.
5. Size and type of conduits.
6. Use of Underwriters' Laboratories *approved* materials and equipment.

There are many others, but those listed above will suffice for the purpose of illustration.

150

Safety Engineering

This is an activity that encompasses several specialties requiring in depth knowledge of mechanical engineering. While the several specialist plan examiners may not be engineers, it is likely that the head of this activity will be a professional engineer.

Several *codes* may be enforced by this group and, depending on the kinds of equipment to be installed, design specifications will be checked against code requirements in some or all of the following areas:

1. Combustion equipment (including air pollution control devices).
2. Boilers and pressure vessels.
3. Air-conditioning and refrigeration equipment.
4. Hoists, dumbwaiters, elevators and escalators.

It seems proper to observe at this point that it is impractical and economically unfeasible for a small code enforcement agency to employ full-time specialists in all of these areas. However, the responsibility of the agency is not lessened by this fact.

External Agencies

All of the specialist plan examiners discussed up to this point would normally be employees of a major city code enforcement agency. In addition there are two other agencies having code enforcement responsibilities, that are usually bureaus or divisions of other departments, having prime interests other than code enforcement. They are the fire marshal and the sanitarian. In a few cities plan examiners from these agencies are stationed in the prime code enforcement agency for the convenience of the public and to facilitate the coordination of code enforcement activities. Unfortunately, this situation is the exception rather than the rule. In most cases plans are not even automatically routed to these agencies but must be hand carried to them by the architect before the building permit can be issued.

The Fire Marshal

The plan examiner representing the fire marshal checks plans for conformity to the fire prevention code and any other code or ordinance that has been assigned to the fire marshal for enforcement.

151

Plans are checked by the fire marshal's plan examiner for the purpose of determining that the design specifications provide the special protective features, devices and equipment required by the fire prevention code and other applicable ordinances for the specific occupancy or occupancies involved.

The Sanitarian

The code requirements of concern to the health department are generally those that pertain to the facilities and equipment found in buildings used for food processing and handling, and those used for the care of human beings and other animals. Some misguided and unfortunate local governments assign housing code enforcement to the health department.

The sanitarian assigned to plan examination duties checks plans to determine that the design specifications provide for the facilities and equipment required by the applicable codes and ordinances for the specific occupancy involved.

Traffic Engineer

The traffic engineer does not normally have code enforcement responsibilities, however, he has a vital interest in any new construction that might substantially affect the traffic flow in the city. A major shopping center with parking spaces for several thousand automobiles is of great concern to him.

Although it may be necessary for him to redesign a major intersection, triple the width of existing streets, and install an entirely new traffic signal system, he normally has no legal control over the *internal* traffic of the shopping center. His authority is usually limited to the determination of the location of the points of access and exit to and from the public thoroughfare.

Since it is in the best interest of the city and the developer to have the street improvements completed at the same time as the shopping center, both parties are usually highly cooperative. In many cases the developer voluntarily pays all the costs of the street improvements.

The Sub-Contractors

Even though a building permit has been issued to a general contractor and the plans to be followed by all of the various tradesmen have been approved, only the general construction work can be started. Each sub-contractor in the *mechanical trades* such as electrical, plumbing, heating, etc., must now take out his own permit to perform the work that has been approved by the plan examiners.

John Q. Citizen

We have followed two *big time operators* through a code enforcement agency but what about the *little guy*, the home owner who wants to build his own garage or complain about his neighbor or who has a violation notice for finishing his attic or recreation room without a permit?

The Garage Builder

Our amateur garage builder will be greeted by the same information clerk who greeted our shopping center architect, he will be given the proper applications and instructed in how to fill them out. When he has filled out the applications, he will present them to the zoning plan examiner who will check the zoning district, the set back and the lot coverage and if they are acceptable, approve the application. If the garage is to be of ordinary frame or masonry construction, the applicant will be given a printed instruction sheet that includes drawings of construction details and a list of specific code requirements. If an unusual design is to be used, the applicant will be asked to provide working drawings to be checked by the structural engineer. The application will then be presented to the permit clerk who will type the permit and direct the applicant to the cashier, who upon payment of the prescribed fee, will issue a receipt and validate the permit. Construction can then be started.

The Complainer

Our citizen with a complaint will be greeted by a receptionist who will ask what the problem is and the address of the property involved. She will then check the department records for that address and if there are any, deliver the file to a supervisor. The citizen will then be introduced to the supervisor, and they will discuss the complaint.

Why go through all of this routine just to record a citizen's complaint? There are many very good reasons, the first of which is

153

public relations. If a citizen is so upset about something that he has taken the trouble to visit city hall in order to complain, he does not want to be brushed off by a receptionist or counter clerk. He wants to talk to someone with authority. Second, the department records may reveal information that will immediately satisfy the complainant or make recording his complaint unnecessary, such as:

1. The complaint has already been made by another citizen and is being investigated.
2. The complaint has been investigated and a violation notice issued, or no cause for action was found.
3. The complaint has been investigated, a violation notice issued and court action is pending.

The supervisor may discover, in questioning the complainant, that the situation complained about is not covered by any ordinance and there is no reason to make an investigation. The last situation obviously calls for a thorough knowledge of municipal ordinances and considerable tact and diplomacy on the part of the supervisor.

If the complaint is a legitimate one and the ordinance or ordinances involved are enforced by the code enforcement agency, the supervisor records the complaint and as much pertinent information as he can get from the complainant. The complaint will then be assigned to an inspector for investigation.

The Violator

The home owner who finished his attic without a permit and got caught will find the path to legitimacy as smooth or as rough as his approach toward the employees of the code enforcement agency who must guide him. If he is belligerent, he is in for a very bad time and will probably wind up in court. On the other hand, if he is pleasant and cooperative, he will probably be surprised at the friendly help he is given.

This appears to be the proper place to point out that ordinary citizens who have never met a politician, let alone having an *in* with one, can and do receive special concessions and waivers of code requirements when the conditions involved are not actually dangerous. This is exactly the kind of situation that Charles S. Rhyne had in mind when he observed that the code enforcement officer must to some extent exercise his own judgement in deciding compliance with the code.

Let us look at some of the violations that may have been built into the attic room that was finished without a permit.

1. Stairway headroom—6'-8" required—6'-5" provided.
2. Ceiling height—7'-6" required—7'-4" provided.
3. Window glass area—20 sq. ft. required—16 sq. ft. provided.
4. Electrical convenience outlets—5 required—4 provided.

Now let us look at the circumstances of the citizen who created these violations. He is a foreign born factory worker who speaks English poorly. He has a large family and the boys have been sleeping in the unfinished attic which is as cold as a refrigerator in winter and hot as an oven in summer. He can afford to buy insulation and wallboard and is capable of installing it himself, but he is not capable of drawing the plans needed to secure a permit and an architect's fee would equal the cost of the materials. He has a friend who works as an electrician at the factory, but is not licensed as a contractor, who is willing to help him with the wiring. He finished the attic and is justifiably proud of his good work, but he did not take out permits for the construction or the wiring and there are violations, even though they are not dangerous.

Our do-it-yourselfer arrives at the reception desk of the code enforcement agency with a legal notice of violations in his hand that says:

1. Dismantle and remove the insulation and wallboard installed in the attic without a permit.
2. Disconnect and remove all electrical wiring installed without a permit.
3. Vacate and desist in the use of the attic for human habitation.
4. Call for inspection upon compliance.

Failure to comply with this notice will be sufficient cause for entering a complaint in ordinance court.

He is a very frightened and worried citizen.

The receptionist takes the violation notice and delivers it along with the department records to a supervisor who reviews the inspection reports and then advises the violator of alternative means of compliance. In this case, it would be almost inhuman to insist on strict conformity to code requirements and an agency that took such an approach would in all likelihood merely pass the responsibility to exercise sound judgement on to the court.

The supervisor in this case, noting from the inspection report that the actual deficiencies were very minor and that no dangerous conditions were involved, suggested that the citizen apply for a permit and instructed him in how to fill out the application and draw plans in sufficient detail so that a permit could be issued. He also attached a list of the violations to the application for the information of the plan examiner. The plan examiner noted the deficiencies on his correction sheet and informed the citizen that he did not have the authority to waive the requirements but suggested that the application be taken to the chief inspector. The chief inspector waived the deficiencies and noted his reasons for doing so on the application as a part of the department's permanent records and the permit was issued. *A private citizen with no political connections had been accorded courteous and special consideration simply because the code administrator had the courage to exercise sound judgement.*

The License Applicant

There is one more code enforcement agency *customer* to be considered. He is the tradesman who must be licensed by the agency.

Comprehensive code enforcement agencies examine and license plumbers, electricians, refrigeration and heating contractors, television repairmen, boiler operators, structural welders, steeplejacks and many others. Where there is a large volume of applicants, special examiners are used, however, it is more common for examinations to be administered by agency supervisory personnel. Examinations may be written or oral or both.

Records

The permanent contribution of the code enforcement agency is its record system. File clerks may be in the agency's lowest pay bracket, but the accuracy and thoroughness with which they do their job is essential to the long term effectiveness of the work done by the administrators, engineers and technicians.

156

A code enforcement agency is no better than its records. In this chapter, we have seen some of the operations carried out in the office of a code enforcement agency. In Chapter XIV, we will look at field operations.

Field Inspections

IN Chapter XIII, we observed that efficient plan examination, coupled with accurate permanent records, was the key to effective code enforcement. In this chapter, we shall see that plan examination, if not followed up by thorough field inspection, is as worthless as plans that are never used.

Without a systematic inspection program and competent inspectors effective code enforcement can never be attained.

One of the few states that has a state-wide building code has been faithfully checking construction plans for years, however, it has no field inspectors. The record of preventable disasters, such as explosions, major fires and structural collapse in that state is one of the worst in the nation. The people have been lulled into thinking that the state is providing them a protection that it is not. Knowledgeable inspectors from other parts of the country who have had occasion to pass through that state are appalled by the number of obvious violations that exist in almost every building that is frequented by the general public. When a contractor in that state has his plans stamped "approved" by the state plan examiner, he can laugh all the way to the bank because there will never be an inspector on the job to see that the building construction actually conforms to the state approved plans.

The need for competent inspectors and systematic code enforcement has never been greater than it is today. Not only are more complex construction methods and systems being used and more sophisticated equipment being installed, but the whole architect, engineer, general contractor, sub-contractor, owner relationship is in a state of flux. Responsibility for the actual performance of any of the functions necessary to the completion of a construction project is dependent upon the contractual agreements between those involved, however, insofar as a code enforcement agency is concerned, the person[1] to whom a permit is issued, is responsible in toto for the work authorized by the permit. The above statement notwithstanding, since real property is always involved in construction, the owner of record of the real property has ultimate responsibility. He has ultimate responsibility for two reasons; first, the permit is issued to the contractor as agent for the owner; second, if a condition is created because of the construction or failure to complete construction, whereby, the city must act, and thereby incur costs to alleviate a dangerous condition, the costs will be assessed against and become a lien upon, the real property.

If a contractor should fail to complete his work, he could be cited in criminal court for a code violation, but the owner would have to seek redress in a civil action.

Changing Contractural Relations

At an earlier time in our history, the architect had prime responsibility, not only for designing a building, but for supervising construction and certifying to the owner that all work had been completed according to plans and specifications and that all contracts had been fulfilled. This is seldom the case today.

In the *good old days*, an owner would engage an architect for a fee which was an agreed upon percentage of the total cost of the project. For this fee, he would design the building, assist in letting the contracts, supervise construction and certify to the owner that all work had been properly completed. Few *owners* are naive enough to *buy this bag* today. In fact, it is almost exclusively those *owners* in the *public sector,* such as state and local governments, institutions of higher learning and school districts that still engage in this archaic practice. Apparently only the taxpayers can afford the luxury of this arrangement.

The New Breed

Today we have what have come to be known as *owner-de-*

---

[1] This could also be a company or a corporation.

velopers. These *owners* in the *private sector* do not *engage* architects and engineers on a fee basis, they hire them and put them on their payrolls. There is a substantial difference between the practicing architect-client relationship and the employer-employee architect relationship that makes the increasing use of the latter arrangement a negative factor in code enforcement.

An employee architect does not have the same authority as one in private practice and he has no effective control over deviations from his plans that occur during the course of construction if the owner approves of them, even if they are code violations.

In addition to having architects and engineers on their payrolls, the owner-developers act as their own general contractors. If they are big enough, they do not even advertise for bids from sub-contractors but instead they tell the sub-contractors how much they will pay for their services. Many sub-contractors faced with this problem extend the *modus operandi* to their employees and although they are technically paid by the hour, they are actually paid on a piece work basis. This practice is sometimes called *lumping* and it has the advantage to the *owner-developer* and the sub-contractor of a fixed cost. It has disadvantages to the tradesman and code enforcement agency, however. If the tradesman experiences difficulty he may be working for a very low hourly wage. The disadvantage to the code enforcement agency is that everyone must work at maximum speed in order to *make out*.

The main reason that there is a greater need for thorough inspection and effective code enforcement in the United States today than ever before in our history is our almost total use of the sub-contractor system. Every workman is in a hurry, he has to be. Even if he is being paid by the hour, if he doesn't produce, his employer cannot stay in business. Our entire construction industry operates on a *get in and get out* philosophy. Few tradesmen, even those who would like to, take pride in their work. Under these circumstances, can anyone doubt the need for competent inspectors and effective code enforcement agencies?

Owner's Interests
The owner's interests are not always in the public interest

and although the architects and engineers on his payroll may design according to code requirements, he might not build according to the design unless ordered to do so by the code enforcement agency. We will cite an example here that is based on an actual case:

An owner-developer built a race track complex that included a large grandstand and clubhouse. The plans were drawn by a registered architect and inspections were made during the course of construction and a certificate of occupancy was issued by the local building inspector, who had formerly been a carpenter working on house construction. About ten years later, business was so good at the race track that the owner decided to double the size of the grandstand and clubhouse. The plans for the addition were drawn by the same registered architect who had designed the original structure. He used exactly the same design and details as before.

The owner-developer built the addition exactly the same as the original, but this time he had a problem. The problem was that he had not fireprotected his steel columns in either the original structure or in the addition. The building code required the protection and the architect had included the details of the protection in the plans, but the owner, not realizing the purpose of enclosing the columns in masonry, had decided not to enclose them because he thought of it only as an unnecessary expense. In this case the architect was engaged only to draw the plans and not to supervise construction. The first building inspector *did not have sufficient knowledge to inspect that type of construction* and he relied on the architect's seal on the plans. The inspector who inspected the addition *was qualified to inspect that type of construction* and he discovered the violation. The city was then placed in the embarrassing position of ordering the fire protection to be placed around the columns in both the addition and the ten year old original structure.

As one travels our interstate freeway system from coast to coast and border to border and observes what appear to be exactly the same buildings on all four corners of every major interchange, it is difficult to envision a practicing architect dissipating his creativity by personally supervising their construction. It is not difficult to envision, however, that there is a need for the local governments responsible for the health, safety and general welfare of the people using those buildings to assure themselves that they are properly constructed. *When the prime interest of every tradesman working in construction is to finish in a hurry, there is no substitute for systematic inspection.*

We have used the race track example to illustrate that serious code violations may be overlooked by inspectors who do not have adequate backgrounds for their assignments and that the seal of a registered architect or engineer on the plans does not insure that the construction will be done according to the plans. We have cited the conditions in a state that examines construction plans, but does not make systematic inspections, as an example of an exercise in futility. We shall now consider a *philosophy* and some practices that will eliminate most of the shortcomings of code enforcement that have just been discussed.

A Philosophy for Effective Code Enforcement

1. Code enforcement is necessary and important.
2. Code enforcement is a government responsibility.
3. Codes are not self-enforcing.
4. Code enforcement agencies cannot rely on the *ethics* of *professionals* as a guarantee of code compliance.
5. Code enforcement begins with plan examination, is established by progress inspections and is maintained by periodic inspection until the structure is demolished.
6. Code enforcement is an honorable profession.

Inspection Practices

The plan examiner *checks plans for conformity to code requirements.* The inspector in the field *must use the plans approved by the plan examiner as the basis for his inspection.*

An inspector in the field does not need the in depth knowledge of the plan examiner, nor does he need the skills of the tradesman on the job. He does have to be able to read the approved plans and he does have to have sufficient knowledge of code requirements in his particular specialty to apply them to situations that are not covered in detail by the plans and specifications. *It is the responsibility of the field inspector to see that work is accomplished in accordance with the approved plans and code requirements.*

One thing an inspector needs in order to make a worthwhile inspection is a set of approved plans. One thing he does not need is a contractor to escort him through the building and interfere with his observations.

Inspection practices vary substantially, depending on the size of the code enforcement agency and the size and complexity of the building, equipment or installation involved. Progress inspections can be divided into two general types which are:

1. *Called* inspections, which means that the general contractor or one of the sub-contractors has completed work up to a certain point and cannot proceed until the work has been inspected and approved. The point of progress at which inspections are required is predetermined either by code or ordinance provisions or by rules established by the code enforcement agency. Contractors working regularly in one jurisdiction soon become well acquainted with the established procedures, but it behooves every contractor working in a strange area to find out what the rules are before he starts to work.

2. *Discretionary* inspection, which means that contractors are not required to call for an inspection at any specific point in progress but the work may be inspected at any time at the discretion of the inspector. *Discretionary* or *surprise* inspections may also be made even when *called* inspections are required.

Dwellings

The *called* inspection method is used principally in the construction of one- and two-family dwellings and *garden* type apartments. In the construction of "high-rise" apartments and other major buildings, the *discretionary* method is more common. Some of the reasons for using different methods of inspection for what might be called *minor* or *major* construction will be explained, however, the prime reason is the difference in the scheduling requirements of the general contractor.

In house construction there are certain natural breaking points in the construction process that are, to a certain extent, convenient times for inspections to be made. It is no coincidence that progress inspections are usually made by code enforcement agencies at the same time that the general contractor has to make an inspection to determine if one sub-contractor has completed his work so that he can call in the next. The code enforcement inspector making progress inspections is, in this respect, an aide to the general contractor.

Let us look at the stages in house construction progress at which inspections are usually made.

- *Basement or foundation*—The sequence of construction operations requires that the excavation around the perimeter of the foundation wall be backfilled before framing can begin. In order to avoid the possibility of re-excavating, the general contractor must assure himself that the foundation walls are of proper size, materials, configuration and are properly located on the property. He must also know that the drain tile has been properly installed and the walls waterproofed. Sewer connections in the excavated area must be properly made. These are exactly the things that the building and plumbing inspectors will be checking before the general contractor is given an OK to backfill. If errors or omissions are discovered, the general contractor will have to call the sub-contractor back to make corrections before he can proceed. It is not unusual for general contractors to withhold payments to sub-contractors until their work has been inspected and approved by the code enforcement agency.

- *Framing*—The most critical stage of house construction occurs just prior to application of the wallboard. The bones, joints, veins, arteries, respiratory systems and disposal tract will be forever hidden from view once the walls are sealed unless an exploratory operation is required to investigate a symptom of some congenital defect.

  Before sealing the walls, the general contractor must be assured that the carpenter, plumber, electrician and heating contractors have all completed that portion of their work that will be concealed. A fully staffed code enforcement agency will have an inspector specialist in each of these trades. If the general contractor overlooks something that should have been done by a sub-contractor, one of the specialist inspectors should find it.

- *Final or pre-occupancy*—Experienced home builders in-

165

sist that all final inspections be made by the code enforcement agency and that a *Certificate of Occupancy* be issued by the jurisdiction before they will release a new house to its purchaser. Those who do not are inviting trouble, not only with the code enforcement agency, but with the purchaser.

Final inspection is made prior to occupancy to determine that all required work has been completed and that the plumbing, electrical, heating and possibly air-conditioning systems are installed and operating properly. Utility companies in many jurisdictions (in all where there is effective code enforcement) will not turn on the utility until authorized to do so by the code enforcement agency.

Knowledgeable home builders have two very good reasons for insisting that final inspections be made in addition to the fact that codes usually require it. First, it is sometimes difficult to get sub-contractors to come back and make repairs after they have been paid in full. By withholding payment until the final inspection has been made, the general contractor maintains the greatest leverage available for securing compliance. Second, and more important, is that a home owner normally has no contact with inspectors and never thinks of the inspections involved in the construction of his home. Even when he is dissatisfied, his complaints are directed only to the home builder. The thought of complaining to the city never occurs to him. However, if final inspections are made after he has been living in the new house for several days or weeks and has had time to discover some of its flaws, his complaints will be made to the inspectors.

If his complaints are justified, violation notices will be issued to the home builder and/or the sub-contractors. If, on the other hand, as is frequently the case, his complaints are justified in terms of his agreement with the home builder *but are not violations of any code or ordinance,* the inspector can take no action and the home owner will suspect collusion between the inspector and the builder.

Code enforcement agencies that do not rigidly enforce final inspection and certificate of occupancy requirements and home builders who do not insist on final inspections and certificates of occupancy before permitting their houses to be occupied are doing each other a great disservice.

166

Minor Buildings

Inspections are generally made on minor buildings such as sheds and private garages at the convenience of the code enforcement agency. Since there are no hidden structural elements or concealed wiring or plumbing, there is no urgency about the timing of inspections, however, inspections are usually made at a specified time upon request.

Major Buildings

Progress inspections made during the course of construction of major buildings are usually assigned to the best qualified and experienced inspectors available in each specialty. The critical nature of scheduling construction operations is such that the use of a *called inspection* system is impractical. Inspectors assigned to what they properly identify with pride as *heavy construction* usually work a *beat*; they are assigned to cover all major construction in a certain district or if they are particularly well versed in special types of construction such as reinforced concrete, or structural steel, or heavy timber, they may be assigned to cover all buildings using that type of construction.

Inspectors working on major building construction are responsible for making necessary inspections *when it is possible for them to be made without interfering with the construction schedule,* unless violations are discovered. In order to do this, inspectors may visit a job site for several hours every day at critical stages in construction and they will *of necessity establish a close liaison with the project supervisor and other appropriate supervisory personnel.* Inspectors assigned to this type of work must have considerable freedom to arrange their own schedules.

Existing Buildings

One more area of field inspection that warrants special mention is the inspection of existing buildings. All of the knowledge that is called upon in the inspection of new construction is called upon in the inspection of existing buildings. If it is important to regulate construction in the first place, it is equally important to regulate the maintenance and use of that construction. While the basic knowledge required of inspectors is

167

the same, the problems they are confronted with and the solutions to those problems are different.

Inspectors working on new construction are dealing with construction people and their approval or disapproval determines whether construction progress continues or stops.

Inspectors working on existing buildings, however, are usually not dealing with people knowledgeable in construction and their task is one of motivating laymen to maintain, repair or alter that which has already been constructed.

In Chapter XV, we shall examine some of the code enforcement methods used for new construction and existing buildings.

Code Enforcement

THE ingredients of an effective code enforcement program are the same regardless of the code that is being enforced, the size of the code enforcement agency or the kind of inspection that reveals a violation. In Chapter XIV, we divided *progress* inspections into two types, which we termed *called* and *discretionary*. The inspection of existing buildings, structures or equipment can properly be called *maintenance* inspection. There are three types of maintenance inspections, namely; *periodic, complaint* and *survey*. Inspections, then, are broken down into kinds and types as follows:

1. Progress Inspections
   a. called
   b. discretionary
2. Maintenance Inspections
   a. periodic
   b. complaint
   c. survey

Periodic inspections are those that are made routinely at time intervals established either by ordinance or policy.

Complaint inspections are made as the result of a citizen's complaint to the code enforcement agency that an unlawful condition exists.

Survey inspections are those made of all buildings within a designated area. (This is the type used in concentrated code enforcement programs.)

In Chapter XIII, we stressed the importance of plan examination and proper records. The basis for inspection, in the case of new construction, is the approved plans and specifications. The

169

basis for inspection, in the case of existing buildings, is the records of the code enforcement agency.[1]

An effective code enforcement program must be designed to prevent violations to the greatest extent possible and to totally abate those which occur in spite of the preventive measures taken. All of the activities of a code enforcement agency can be conveniently divided into those that are directed toward *preventing* violations and those that are directed toward *abating* violations.

The records compiled as part of the activities directed towards preventing violations are essential to those activities that are necessary to secure abatement of violations that do occur. Conversely, the reports filed as part of the abatement activities become part of the records necessary for effective prevention of violations.

In order to illustrate all of the procedures involved in effective code enforcement, we shall have to use two examples. One example will illustrate the processing of a violation occurring during the course of a building's construction and the other will cite the circumstances involved in processing a violation discovered during inspection of an existing building.

Before citing our first example, it is important that we point out that in code enforcement we are not concerned about the details of what is *right* about a situation. A simple OK followed by the date and inspector's initials (if he is a competent inspector) is an indication that everything is acceptable. Only when something is *wrong* do we need a written statement. *When something is wrong, we need a concise narrative statement of fact. A check list is wholly inadequate.*

Some code enforcement agencies, especially those that are experimenting with data processing equipment, burden their inspectors with bed sheet size, paper ballot type report forms that appear to have as many boxes for the inspector to check as the data processing equipment is capable of accommodating. This might be good for the data processing equipment industry but its contribution to code enforcement is negative since the inspector is so preoccupied with putting check marks in little boxes he is liable to overlook serious code violations.

---

[1] Agency records may include copies of the original plans and specifications. Policies vary widely on this but many agencies keep the plans for major buildings indefinitely.

A Construction Violation

A building inspector making a *called* first inspection on a dwelling observed that the North basement foundation wall was only two feet from the property line. The approved plans called for three feet as did the building code, the housing code and the zoning ordinance. He made the following notation on his field report: Violation—North side yard 2', 3' required. The report was dated and initialed. Separately, he wrote a *Field Violation Notice* which directed the builder to—1. Provide the required 3' North side yard as per plan. 2. Call for inspection upon compliance. The original copy of the field violation notice was presented to the builder; two copies of the notice were retained by the inspector, one was attached to the inspector's field report until compliance or until a superseding notice would be issued, the other would be returned to the office and kept in an active file until compliance was secured.

It is not a simple matter to relocate a basement and the builder was understandably upset. He decided to see if he could get the side yard deficiencies waived. When the inspector returned to the office in the afternoon, the builder was there appealing to his supervisor. In this jurisdiction, the building commissioner had discretionary authority to waive minor deviations from the building code and housing code, but he had no authority to waive requirements of the zoning ordinance. Slight mislocation of buildings is not uncommon and because the inspectors in his department were well trained, closely supervised and had no authority to exercise discretion on their own, it was quite common for the commissioner to exercise his discretionary authority. The commissioner was not arbitrary in exercising his discretion, however, and had established his own standards for typical situations involving waiver requests. In the case of side yards, his limit was four inches. He would automatically waive deficiencies up to four inches, but those greater than that would not be waived. His rulings were based on the conditions involved, rather than on the personalities involved. The commissioner also had an open door policy and was willing to discuss any problem with any citizen who asked specifically to see him. In this case, the supervisor was aware of the commissioner's standards on side yard waivers and he explained them to the builder. The

171

builder asked to see the commissioner nevertheless, and his request for a waiver was denied.

Had the commissioner waived the side yard requirements of the building code and housing code, it would still have been necessary for the builder to seek a waiver from the Zoning Board of Appeals for the side yard deficiencies under the requirements of the Zoning Ordinance. The Zoning Board of Appeals had a firm policy in this jurisdiction however, that all waivers required prior to the issuance of a permit must be secured prior to appeal to the Zoning Board. This policy was established because previously persons granted zoning variances had still been unable to secure permits because of other ordinances.

The builder, in this case, had exhausted his remedies, other than an appeal to the court, and would have to comply. He decided to comply, however there were some complicating factors that had to be resolved. He had not paid the subcontractor who had actually built the basement in the wrong location and the subcontractor not only refused to return and rebuild the basement, but he had also blacklisted the builder with the masonry contractors association. The builder could not hire anyone to rebuild the basement properly so he had no alternative but to bring suit against the subcontractor, which he did. Lawsuits take time, and stalled unattended construction projects are attractive but hazardous play sites for children.

The loose soil around this basement excavation caved in and blocked the sewer. The basement and the excavation around it filled with water which soon became stagnant. The mothers of the neighborhood children could not keep them away from the genuinely dangerous excavation. One of the mothers complained to the building department and thereby started the following activities: A complaint clerk recorded the complaint in duplicate and assigned a complaint number. A file clerk checked the active address file and finding the *open* building permit for the same address given in the complaint, attached the original copy of the complaint to the permit field copy, placed the copy of the complaint in the active address file in place of the permit field copy and put the complaint form and permit field copy (with field violation attached) in the inspector's work for the next day.

When the inspector arrived on the job site and observed its condition, he made the following notations:

1. On the field copy of the permit he noted "Field violation not complied, excavation filled with stagnant water".
2. On the inspector's copy of the field violation notice he noted— "Violation not complied, new violation. Recommend supersede with legal notice".
3. On the complaint form he wrote the following report and recommendation: "Inspection reveals basement excavation dug under permit #12345 is filled with stagnant water and is an invitational hazard to neighborhood children. Field violation notice #67890 to provide the required 3' North side yard has not been complied with. Job has been idle for 30 days.

"Recommend supersede field violation notice with legal notice of violations as follows: 1. Provide the required 3' North side yard as per plan and permit #12345 or backfill the open dangerous excavation and grade the lot level. B115.2, 115.3, 115.4, 125.3"[2]

The inspector signed the inspection report and turned it in at the end of the day with the rest of his work. The work turned in by the inspector was sorted out by a clerk who filed all field reports that did not require any further action and delivered all reports that did require action to the inspector's supervisor for review and approval of the action recommended by the inspector.

The supervisor reviewed the inspector's report for thoroughness and accuracy and after determining that it was properly written and that the code section numbers cited by the inspector as authority for each item on the recommended notice were in order, approved the report for typing.

The typist, using the information contained in the inspector's report, typed the following Notice of Violations on printed forms in quadruplicate that were designed for that purpose:

NOTICE OF VIOLATIONS

NAME John Doe Date 8/18/69

ADDRESS 1313 E. 60th Street

THE DEPARTMENT OF BUILDINGS, AS REQUIRED BY LAW HAS INSPECTED the dwelling under construction LOCATED AT 10 Downing Street. INSPECTED ON 8/17/69

---

[2] The numbers indicated are applicable section numbers of the Building Code which is indicated by the letter "B" before the first number. If it were a plumbing code violation, the letter would be "P", etc.

VIOLATIONS OF THE BUILDING CODE WERE FOUND TO EXIST.

THE FOLLOWING ORDERS ARE ISSUED FOR THE CORRECTION OF THESE VIOLATIONS AND SHALL BE COMPLIED WITH ON OR BEFORE 8/28/69 OTHERWISE COURT ACTION MAY BE INSTITUTED.

WARNING:—DAMAGE OR INJURY RESULTING FROM DELAY OR FAILURE TO COMPLY WITH THIS NOTICE WILL BE ATTRIBUTED TO NEGLIGENCE ON THE PART OF THE RESPONSIBLE PARTY OR PARTIES. NOTIFY THIS DEPARTMENT UPON COMPLIANCE OF THIS VIOLATION.

Provide the required 3′ North side yard as per plan and permit #12345 or backfill the open dangerous excavation and grade the lot level. B115.2, 115.3, 115.4, 125.3.

IN REPLY REFER TO NOTICE BB98765 INSPECTOR Jones District 83

DIRECT PHONE INQUIRIES TO W. J. Brown, Supervisor TELEPHONE 748-4000, EXTENSION 248

The notice was mailed to the builder and the copies were distributed as follows: one copy was attached to the inspector's field copy of the building permit and filed in a date file for re-inspection on the compliance date. One copy was placed in the open address file where it would remain until the violation was cleared. The final copy was bound in a book of violation notices in numerical sequence as a permanent record and for auditing purposes.

On the compliance date, the inspector's copy was removed from the date file and he reinspected the job site. Inspection revealed that nothing had been done and the inspector wrote the date and the notation "Not complied" on his copy of the violation notice. What the inspector did next resulted in early compliance with the violation notice and it demonstrated that he had been trained to exhaust every effort to secure compliance before resorting to court action.

When the inspector returned to the office at the end of the day, he called the builder and explained that the neighborhood children were playing in the water filled basement excavation and that unless the dangerous condition was eliminated by the builder, the city would have to backfill the excavation and assess the costs against the property. He suggested that the builder pump the water out of the excavation and renew his efforts to get the basement rebuilt in the proper location. The builder agreed to pump the water out the next day and he said that the preliminary hearing would be held the following week on his lawsuit with the subcontractor.

The inspector added the following note to his copy of the violation notice, "Contacted builder by phone, he promised to pump water out of excavation tomorrow and said that court hearing with subcontractor would be held next week". He did not turn this report in with the rest of his work but held it for reinspection the next day. Inspection the next day revealed that the water had been pumped out so he dated his report and made the following entry, "Water pumped out, dangerous condition eliminated. Recommend hold 10 days for results of court hearing." The report was turned in to his supervisor at the end of the day and the supervisor initialed the report as an indication that he accepted the inspector's recommendation. The file clerk placed the report in the date file where it would remain for 10 days unless it were removed earlier because of a *called* inspection.

At the court hearing the following week, the builder and the subcontractor settled their differences in the judge's chambers. The subcontractor rebuilt the basement walls in the proper location and the builder called for re-inspection.

A file clerk pulled the violation notice and inspector's field copy of the building permit from the date file and placed it with the inspector's work for the following day. On re-inspection, the inspector found everything in order and made the following notations: on the building permit field copy he wrote the date and "Violation complied. OK to backfill", and on the violation notice he wrote the date and "Complied". He signed the reports and turned them in with his work at the end of the day. A file clerk returned the permit field copy to the active address file, removed the copy of the violation notice from the file and placed the inspector's copy of the violation notice in a *history* file.

When the next inspection is called, the inspector will be given only the field copy of the building permit because the violation notice that had been complied with is no longer relevant.

We brought our example of a construction violation to a happy ending because at the point where compliance cannot be

175

secured without instituting court procedures, the processing of construction violations and existing building violations become the same.

Our example of an existing building violation will be carried all the way to court and beyond.

An Existing Building Violation

A citizen called the code enforcement agency and complained that her next door neighbor was operating a beauty shop in her home. The complaint clerk wrote the address and this notation on a complaint form in duplicate: "Complaint—Operating beauty shop in one-family dwelling." She then checked the active address file and, finding no *open* permits or violation notices, assigned a complaint number, placed a copy of the complaint in the active file and placed the original complaint form in the work to be assigned to field inspectors for the next day.

When the inspector arrived at the site of the alleged violation, he observed that there was a small sign in the living room window which read, "Beauty Shoppe, Phone 975-3100, Please use rear entrance." He was greeted at the rear entrance by a woman in a cosmetologist's uniform. He introduced himself, explained the nature of his visit, and presented his business card. He was invited to inspect the premises and from his observations and conversation with the cosmetologist, he entered the following information on the face of the complaint form:

OWNER—Susan Green

ADDRESS—2216 Boxwood

TENANT—Same

OCCUPANCY—1 Family Dwelling & Beauty Shop

And wrote the following report:

Inspection reveals recreation room in cellar of one family dwelling is used as a commercial beauty shop. Equipment observed consists of two commercial type hair dryers and beauty shop chairs and a display case of cosmetic supplies.

Small sign in living room window advertises "Beauty Shoppe."

Owner has license #907589 issued by the State Board of Cosmetology to operate at this address.

Owner stated that she moved the shop into her home three months ago from a commercial location because she is a divorcee and could not afford to pay high commercial rent and hire a full time baby-sitter for her children. She also stated that she did not know anything about the zoning ordinance and assumed that when the State Board of Cosmetology issued her license she had cleared all legal obstacles.[3]

The inspector thanked the owner for her cooperation and left for his next stop. (He did not tell her what action he would have to take because at that point he could not know for certain. Before he could write his recommendations he would have to check the department's records and then his recommendation would have to be approved by his supervisor).

On returning to the office, the inspector checked the permit records[4] (only the active file had been checked by the complaint clerk) and added the following information to his report:

Building constructed under permit #78395-1954 for one family dwelling. Permit #83363-1957 issued for private garage and permit #58623-1963 to finish recreation room in the cellar. No other permits have been issued.

He also checked the zoning maps and noted on the face of the complaint form that the property was located in an R-1 zoning district (one family dwellings) as indicated on map #36.

He then made his recommendations as follows:

Recommend Notice:

1. Cease and desist in the use of a one family dwelling as a one family dwelling and beauty shop and restore to its legal use as a one family dwelling only. Z 10.1
2. Remove the advertising sign from the living room window. Z 10.1.

His report was processed in exactly the same manner as in our previous example and the cosmetologist was sent the notice

---

[3] One of the real sticky problems in local government code enforcement is that there is little or no liaison between local government agencies and state agencies. Formal clearance procedures are rare and a state agency that requires local government approval, prior to issuance of a state license, is the exception rather than the rule. The typical attitude of state agency administrators appears to be: "Let local government look out for themselves, we have enough problems of our own."

[4] It is frequently necessary for inspectors assigned to existing building work to spend more time in the office doing research and contacting violators than they spend in the field.

that he had recommended. Since this was not a hazardous situation, she was given 30 days to comply.

When she received the notice, she called the inspector's supervisor who explained why the inspector had not told her at the time of the inspection that she would receive a violation notice. He also explained that she had a right to appeal to the Zoning Board of Appeals and that, although he did not want to encourage her, if she wanted to appeal he would assist her in filling out the necessary applications.

She decided to appeal and this is what followed:

1. The supervisor assisted her in filling out an application for a permit for a change of occupancy from a one family dwelling to a one family dwelling and a beauty shop.

2. He provided information from department records that would be needed by the plan examiners.

3. He secured a *tentative* approval from the structural plan examiner that if the Zoning Board granted her appeal it would be possible for a permit to be issued under building code requirements.

4. He introduced her to the zoning plan examiner who provided her with a formal written rejection of her application for a change of occupancy permit and who assisted her in filling out the forms used in filing an appeal.

5. The cosmetologist then paid a small filing fee and filed for an appeal with the secretary of the zoning board of appeals, who assigned a hearing date for the appeal.

6. The secretary of the zoning board of appeals placed the case on the docket for the assigned date and notified the code enforcement agency.

7. The code enforcement agency noted the date of the hearing on the inspector's copy of the violation notice, extended the compliance date until the day after the hearing and placed the violation notice in the date file for that date.

8. The zoning board of appeals, after public hearing, denied the appeal and notified both the applicant and the code enforcement agency of their action in writing.

9. The inspectors field copy of the violation notice was removed from the date file. The action taken by the zoning board was noted and the notice was returned to the inspector to follow up.

From the time the cosmetologist had filed for appeal, further action by the code enforcement agency had been stayed. Denial of the appeal by the zoning board signaled continuation of the enforcement process.

There was no need to make a re-inspection at this early date since there had not been time for compliance. The inspector called the cosmetologist on the telephone, said he was sorry that her appeal had been denied, and asked when he could expect compliance. She replied that she needed time to find a nearby location that she could afford and that she had already booked appointments for the next two weeks. She asked if thirty days extension could be granted. The inspector replied that thirty days seemed a little excessive but if she removed the sign from the living room window immediately, he would recommend to his supervisor that the compliance date be extended for thirty days. She agreed that this was reasonable; the inspector drove by the next day, noted that the sign was gone and recommended a thirty day extension. His supervisor accepted his recommendation and the inspector's copy of the violation notice went back in the date file for another thirty days.

In about three weeks the inspector received a call from the cosmetologist who reported that she had closed out her business and had taken a job in another beauty shop. She requested that he make a reinspection the next day so that the violation could be cleared from the records.

Inspection the next day revealed that the commercial type hair dryers, beauty shop chairs and cosmetic display case were all stored neatly in a corner of the recreation room. The zoning ordinance did not prohibit the storage of these items in a private residence, in fact, it did not prohibit the use of this equipment by the owner, except for commercial purposes. The appearance of the recreation room and the cosmetologist's statement indicated that she had complied with the violation notice.

The inspector thanked her for her cooperation and left the premises. Once outside the building, he made the following entry on the field copy of the violation notice "Beauty shop equipment consisting of two commercial type hair dryers, two beauty shop chairs and a cosmetics display case stored in corner of recreation room. Violation appears to be complied, however, recommend reinspect to verify in ninety days." His supervisor accepted his recommendation and the notice went back in the date file for ninety days.

In about two weeks, the next door neighbor who had made the original complaint called to find out when something was going to be done about the beauty shop next door. She had been at the public hearing when the zoning board had denied the appeal and she wanted some action. The complaint clerk transferred the call to the supervisor and got the field copy of the violation notice from the date file for him. After listening to the complaint the supervisor made the following entry on the notice. "Original complainant called and said that the beauty shop is still being operated and she wants action. Re-inspect."

When the inspector attempted to make an inspection the next day he was denied entry by a very irate cosmetologist who asserted that she was not going to submit to any further harrassment by the city. The inspector made the following entry on the notice: "Refused entry by owner who stated that she will not submit to any further harrassment. Recommend administrative hearing." His supervisor approved his recommendation and the following notice was sent to Cosmetologist Susan Green: "Appear at this office at 10 a.m. Tuesday June 10, 1967 and show cause why a complaint should not be entered against you in ordinance court for violation of Section 10.1, Article X, Ordinance 171d of the compiled ordinances of this city. Failure to appear at the hearing will be sufficient cause for filing the complaint."

Mrs. Green failed to appear at this administrative hearing and the supervisor decided to enter a complaint in ordinance court, however there was no way to prove without entering the building and observing the shop in operation that a violation existed. If a warrant were obtained, the building could be entered but even if the equipment was in use it could not be proven that it was being used commercially.

The supervisor called the complaining neighbor and secured the name of one of the customers of the illegal beauty shop. He then had one of the department typists call and make an appointment to have her hair done, giving the name of the regular customer as a reference. The typist kept the appointment, had her hair done and paid the cosmetologist, Mrs. Green.

The supervisor then entered the court complaint and based on the testimony of the inspector and the typist, Mrs. Green was found guilty as charged, fined $25, and admonished by the judge to cease operating the beauty shop forthwith.

The judge's finding of guilty and assessment of a fine brought this case to a close, however, if Mrs. Green continued to operate the beauty shop she would not be immune from further prosecution. Penalties for ordinance violators are generally assessable for each day that the violation occurs or exists. The code enforcement agency can immediately write a new violation notice and enter a new complaint in court when a violation continues to exist.

We have used two extreme examples of ordinance violations processed by a code enforcement agency in order to bring all of the activities that are involved into focus.

Minor violations that occur routinely during the course of construction are usually corrected immediately. Tradesmen who are licensed by a code enforcement agency cannot risk having their licenses suspended or revoked and some agencies keep a record of violations by contractor as well as by address. If a contractor accumulates too many outstanding violation notices, he is not permitted to take out any more permits until he complies.

In this chapter we have looked at some depth into the detailed operations involved in code enforcement. In chapter XVI we shall attempt to establish the essentials of the code enforcement professional.

The Code Enforcement
Professional

T HIS book is dedicated to the first professional *building official,* however, he was more than that he was a professional *code enforcement* official. The term *building official* has a narrow connotation that obscures both the scope of responsibilities and the nature of the activities of a code enforcement agency. It has caused local governments to staff these agencies with people who are incapable, by virtue of *trained incapacity* or being *fit in an unfit fitness* of ever becoming professional *code enforcement officials.* The term is also a partial cause of the fragmentation of code enforcement activities and the distribution of code enforcement responsibilities, without coordination, throughout several departments.

In spite of a nation-wide tendency to place undue emphasis on the technical backgrounds[1] of code enforcement officials and inspectors while overlooking the character traits and personal qualities that are essential to their success, we do have quite a few professional code enforcement officials and inspectors in the United States today. We used the term *quite a few* because *quite a few* is obviously not enough. There is a desperate need for thousands of professional code enforcement officials and inspectors in this country *right now.*

Those code enforcement officials and inspectors who are in

---

[1] The professional societies and trade unions are the prime advocates of job specifications that limit certain positions in code enforcement agencies to members of their groups. Their narrow interests of *taking care of their own* is the root cause of the inability of many agencies to achieve even a small measure of success in code enforcement.

fact, professionals; have reached that plane because they *identify* with *code enforcement*. They may have been *architects, engineers, lawyers, builders, contractors, carpenters, bricklayers, plumbers, electricians or even grocery clerks and gas station attendants*; but in becoming a *code enforcement professional* they have *rejected* the *values* and *allegiances* required of their previous calling and have accepted those of the present. *They have used their prior training and experience as a foundation and have added a superstructure built of the skills and knowledge that are essential in their new profession.* They have changed their calling early enough to have escaped the trap of *trained incapacity.*

Although the code enforcement professional may be justifiably proud of his academic achievements and the symbols of professional recognition in an earlier calling, *he is equally proud of his current role.* He knows that the physical condition of his jurisdiction is a constantly visible and accurate reflection of the proficiency of his agency.

Those local governments that have code enforcement agencies administered by professional code enforcement officials are usually unaware of their good fortune, because the *effectiveness* and *efficiency* of properly administered agencies keeps them out of the limelight.

Local governments that are plagued with code enforcement problems even though they have staffed their agencies with *professionals* might find on investigation that they have hired the wrong kind of professionals. Professionalism in no other field automatically guarantees professionalism in code enforcement.

No Identifiable Source of Supply

Unfortunately there is no identifiable source of supply of professional code enforcement officials. No institutions of higher learning grant degrees in code enforcement. No professional society attests to the competence of code enforcement officers. And no other training or work experience prepares an individual to be a professional in code enforcement.

In administering the millions of dollars in federal funds that are being channeled into code enforcement programs, the Department of Housing and Urban Development has an obligation to audit the effectiveness of those programs. Local governments must be held accountable, not only for the adoption of acceptable codes and standards, but for their enforcement.

Effective and *efficient* code enforcement requires professionalism, but where is the source of supply or even the raw material? Traditionally we have drawn upon the design professions and the building trades. Those drawn from these sources who were *adaptable* and had the *right personality* make up have become key members of the local government administrative team. Those who could not *adapt* or who had *personality problems* have been dismal failures and are a serious handicap to their administration.

From the start of the depression in the early 1930's until World War II local governments were able to attract exceptionally well qualified people because there were few jobs in private employment. Many of these people enjoyed their work and stayed on after the war even though they could have increased their incomes by returning to private industry. Some of our outstanding code enforcement professionals were developed during this period.

The construction boom that followed World War II caused a rapid expansion of the big city code enforcement agencies and the creation of many new agencies in the suburbs and smaller cities. Most of the code enforcement inspectors and officials hired to staff these agencies were young recently discharged veterans with engineering or building trades backgrounds. Their military training made them responsive to instructions and consequently their earlier trade or engineering backgrounds was an asset rather than a liability.

With well qualified and experienced people as a nucleus, some code enforcement agencies were expanded rapidly into effective cohesive units. Where this kind of agency expansion occurred, the officials and inspectors identified with the agency rather than with a professional society or trade union. A genuine esperit de corp existed within the agency.

At the end of World War II a few well qualified people who had entered local government during the depression were called upon to train several hundred eager young men to be code enforcement officers. There was nothing formal about this, nor was there any coordination. Each community approached the problem in its own way and developed its own methods.

Today there are a few hundred code enforcement officials

and inspectors in the United States who each have approximately a quarter of a century of experience in code enforcement superimposed on whatever pre-entry training or experience they brought to the job.

These are the *code enforcement professionals* who form the nucleus on which we must build a corps of career code enforcement officers that is capable of policing the development, rebuilding and maintenance of our country.

The Raw Material

There is an acute shortage of design professionals and building tradesmen in the United States today. It is no secret that the building trade unions deliberately maintain this shortage through rigid control of their apprenticeship programs and that minority groups find it almost impossible to get in. Minority groups are not the only Americans who have been denied the basic freedom of working at a trade of their choice since in many unions the apprenticeship programs are open only to the relatives of members. *When local governments require that inspectors be building trades journeymen they are compounding this crime against a large segment of our society and they are slamming the door in the face of talent that is badly needed to build our corps of professionals in code enforcement.*

The shortage of design professionals exists for other reasons but it is just as real, nevertheless. The foundation of all engineering is mathematics and increasingly our young people with a mathematical bent have understandably been attracted to those special fields of engineering that offer, not only the highest salaries, but a substantial amount of glamour and excitement.

The construction industry is not competitive, as far as engineers are concerned, either in salaries or glamour with the aero-space and electronics industries and there is little likelihood that it ever will be.

Salaries paid engineers by local governments are far below those paid by industry for positions of comparable responsibility. In addition, engineers in local government are frequently confronted by social problems that they are not prepared to cope with and would not be called upon to cope with in private employment.

Opportunity Knocks

The current shortage of design professionals and building tradesmen is not a crisis in code enforcement, it is an opportunity. It is an opportunity, born of necessity, to staff our code enforcement agencies with code enforcement professionals rather than design professionals and building tradesmen. It is an opportunity to build the corps of professional code enforcement officers that is needed to police the development, rebuilding and maintenance of our country, and it is an opportunity to open the door of participation in a vital government activity to thousands of Americans who have been locked out in spite of their talents and abilities.

Building the Corps

The first step in building our corps is recognizing that code enforcement is a profession in itself, that education, training and experience in no other profession is adequate preparation for professionalism in code enforcement.

The second step is eliminating all requirements that code enforcement officers possess a license in some other trade or profession.

The third step is establishing an open career path in our code enforcement agencies similar to those that exist in our police and fire departments. When a young man embarks on a career as a code enforcement officer he should know that it is possible through outstanding performance to progress through the ranks and eventually become head of the department. He should not have to produce evidence that he has been sprinkled with holy water by an agency or institution outside of his own jurisdiction as proof of his competence.

The fourth step is to bar the door of our code enforcement agencies to those who are *incapable* of becoming code enforcement professionals.

If one is concerned to bring into the leadership ranks of a profession or a class or a society the men best qualified to exercise that leadership, the sensible thing is to guard the door with rigorous selection procedures, rigorous procedures for testing ability, rigorous courses of preparation. The purpose of the rigor is not simply to screen out the less able but to screen out the less highly motivated.

187

The ones who get through will then be not only men of superior ability but men of superior character. The very fact of their surmounting difficult obstacles will have accomplished a vitally important sorting out.[2]

We must determine through pre-entry testing not so much what an applicant has done, but what he is capable of doing, not just from a narrow technological standpoint but from the standpoint of those attributes not measured by aptitude and achievement tests. We must somehow evaluate the almost inmeasurable traits of enthusiasm, judgment, and perseverance that determine success, mediocrity or failure in any pursuit.

The fifth step is to establish as a prototype an American Academy of Code Administration as a separate department within an established university. The Academy should be staffed by qualified code enforcement professionals but its students should also attend appropriate classes in other departments. Graduates of the Academy should be granted a Bachelor of Science Degree in Code Enforcement.

The sixth and final step is the establishment of a meaningful certification program by the Building Officials Conference of America accompanied by an accreditation program for degree granting institutions offering courses in code enforcement. To be meaningful the certification requirements will have to be high and make no provision for certification under a *grandfathers clause.*

Steps five and six may seem inconsistent with the last sentence in step three. They are not intended to be. Local governments should not require either the degree or certification in their job specifications. *Steps five and six are necessary in the national interest to identify those who have demonstrated their competence and to induce the personnel mobility that is an essential part of the development of nationwide professional standards.*

Only two professions in local government, have achieved substantial mobility, *city managers* and *planners*. It is no coincidence that both professions enjoy high prestige and high salaries. **Until code enforcement professionals became identified as such, until they become visible and mobile, and until local governments**

---

[2] John W. Gardner, *Excellence: Can We Be Equal and Excellent Too?* (New York: Harper & Row, Publishers, 1962) , p. 100.

start pirating the outstanding professionals from each other, we will not have *effective* and *efficient* code enforcement in the United States.

Appendixes

APPENDIX A

MODEL CODES STANDARDIZATION COUNCIL (MCSC)

Members

American National Standards Institute

E. A. Weed
Construction Standards Board
10 East 40th Street
New York, New York 10016

Warner Daily, Secretary
Construction Standards Board
10 East 40th Street
New York, New York 10016

Building Officials Conference of America, Inc.

Bernard T. Aschenbrand
Chief Building Inspector
Bergenfield, New Jersey 07621

Richard L. Sanderson, Executive Director
Building Officials Conference of America, Inc.
1313 East 60th Street
Chicago, Illinois 60637

Gaylon Claiborne, Technical Director
Building Officials Conference of America, Inc.
1313 East 60th Street
Chicago, Illinois 60637

International Conference of Building Officials

T. H. (Nick) Carter, Managing Director
International Conference of Building Officials
50 South Los Robles
Pasadena, California 91101

William G. Vasvary, Director
Department of Building
Fullerton, California 92632

National Bureau of Standards

H. Allen Bates, Chief
Office of Engineering Standards Liaison
National Bureau of Standards
U. S. Department of Commerce
Washington, D. C. 20234

G. A. Rowland
Codes and Safety Standards Section
National Bureau of Standards
U. S. Department of Commerce
Washington, D. C. 20234

Irwin Banjaman, Chief
Fire Research
Building Research Division
Institute of Applied Technology
National Bureau of Standards
U. S. Department of Commerce
Washington, D. C. 20234

National Fire Protection Association

Percy Bugbee, General Manager
National Fire Protection Association
60 Batterymarch Street
Boston, Massachusetts 02110

Richard E. Stevens, Director of Engineering
National Fire Protection Association
60 Batterymarch Street
Boston, Massachusetts 02110

191

Underwriters Laboratories, Inc.

H. B. Whitaker
Underwriters Laboratories, Inc.
207 East Ohio Street
Chicago, Illinois 60611

Jack Bono
Underwriters Laboratories, Inc.
207 East Ohio Street
Chicago, Illinois 60611

Observers

American Hospital Association

Arron F. McCrary
American Hospital Association
840 North Lake Shore Drive
Chicago, Illinois 60611

American Institute of Architects

William Scheick, Executive Director
1735 New York Avenue, N.W.
Washington, D. C. 20006

Frank L. Codella, Administrator
Department of Professional Service
1735 New York Avenue, N.W.
Washington, D. C. 20006

American Insurance Association

Everett W. Fowler, Chief Engineer
American Insurance Association
85 John Street
New York, New York 10038

John Jablonsky, Director
Codes and Standards
American Insurance Association
85 John Street
New York, New York 10038

G. M. Watson
American Insurance Association
85 John Street
New York, New York 10038

American Society of Civil Engineers

William H. Correale

333 Jay Street
Brooklyn, New York 11201

James P. Thompson
Southern Pine Association
National Bank of Commerce Building
210 Barrone Street
New Orleans, Louisiana 70112

Building Industry Association Representative

Ashby T. Gibbons
Portland Cement Association
Old Orchard Road
Skokie, Illinois 60076

Building Research Advisory Board

James R. Smith
Building Research Advisory Board
2101 Constitution Avenue, N.W.
Washington, D. C. 20418

Department of Housing and Urban Development

Robert C. Reichel, Chief
Codes and Building Standards Branch
Renewal Assistance Administration
Department of Housing and Urban Development
Washington, D. C. 20413

William S. Brown
Architectural Standards Division
Federal Housing Administration
Department of Housing and Urban Development
Washington, D. C. 20410

National Association of Home Builders

Milton W. Smithman, Director of Technical Services
National Association of Home Builders
1625 L Street, N.W.
Washington, D. C. 20036

Willard E. Bryant, Assistant Director of Technical Services
National Association of Home Builders
1625 L Street, N.W.
Washington, D. C. 20036

National Research Council of Canada

Robert F. Legget, Chairman
Associate Committee on the National Building Code
National Research Council of Canada
Division of Building Research
Ottawa 2, Ontario, Canada

John M. Robertson, Secretary
Associate Committee on the National Building Code

National Research Council of Canada
Division of Building Research
Ottawa 2, Ontario, Canada

Southern Building Code Congress

Hubert N. Caraway, Executive Director
Southern Building Code Congress
1116 Brown-Marx Building
Birmingham, Alabama 35203

APPENDIX B

ACCREDITED AUTHORITATIVE AGENCIES

Concrete

American Concrete Institute
P.O. Box 4754 Redford Station
22400 West Seven Mile Road
Detroit, Michigan 48219.........ACI

Concrete Reinforcing Steel Institute
228 North LaSalle Street
Chicago, Illinois 60601.........CRSI

Gypsum Association
201 North Wells Street
Chicago, Illinois 60606..........GA

National Concrete Masonry Association
2009 Fourteenth Street, North
Arlington, Virginia 22201.....NCMA

National Lime Association
4000 Brandywine Street, NW
Washington, D. C. 20016.......NLA

Portland Cement Association
5420 Old Orchard Road
Skokie, Illinois 60076..........PCA

Electrical

American Institute of Electrical
  Engineers
33 West 39th Street
New York, New York 10018....AIEE

Illuminating Engineers Society
345 East 47th Street
New York, New York 10017......IES

International Association of
  Electrical Inspectors
201 East Erie Street
Chicago, Illinois 60611........IAEI

National Electrical Manufacturers
  Association
155 East 44th Street
New York, New York 10017...NEMA

National Electric Sign Association
10922 South Western Avenue
Chicago, Illinois 60642........NESA

Equipment

Air-Conditioning and Refrigeration
  Institute
1815 North Fort Myer Drive
Arlington, Virginia 22209........ARI

American Gas Association
1032 East 62nd Street
Cleveland, Ohio 44103.........AGA

American Petroleum Institute
1625 K Street, NW
Washington, D. C. 20005........API

American Society of Heating,
  Refrigerating and Air-Conditioning
  Engineers
United Engineering Center
345 East 47th Street
New York, New York 10017..ASHRAE

The American Society of Mechanical
  Engineers
United Engineering Center
345 East 47th Street
New York, New York 10017....ASME

Home Ventilating Institute
1108 Standard Building
Cleveland, Ohio 44113..........HVI

Incinerator Institute of America
60 East 42nd Street-Suite 1914
New York, New York 10017......IIA

The Institute of Boiler and
  Radiator Manufacturers
393 Seventh Avenue-10th Fl.
New York, New York 10001....I-B-R

National Automatic Sprinkler and
  Fire Control Association, Inc.
2 Holland Avenue
White Plains, New York
  10603 ....NASFCA

National Elevator Manufacturing
  Industry, Inc.
101 Park Avenue
New York, New York 10017....NEMI

Equipment—continued

National LP-Gas Association
79 West Monroe Street
Chicago, Illinois 60603.......NLPGA

National Oil Fuel Institute, Inc.
60 East 42nd Street
New York, New York 10017....NOFI

National Environmental Systems
Contractors Association
221 N. LaSalle Street
Chicago, Illinois 60601.......NESCA

Uniform Boiler and Pressure Vessel
Laws Society, Inc.
57 Pratt Street
Hartford, Connecticut 06103.UBPVLS

Government Agencies

Department of Defense
Office of Civil Defense
Office of the Secretary of the Army
Washington, D. C. 20390..DOD-OCD

Federal Aviation Agency
Systems Research and Development
Service
Washington, D. C. 20553.......FAA

Federal Specifications
Superintendent of Documents
Government Printing Office
Washington, D. C. 20234........FS

Forest Products Laboratory
United States Department of
Agriculture
Madison, Wisconsin 53705.......FPL

Housing and Home Finance Agency
Division of Housing Research
Washington, D. C. 20410......HHFA

Joint Army-Navy Specifications
Bureau of Supplies and Accounts
Navy Department
Washington, D. C. 20225
  Air Material Command
  Wright-Patterson Air Force Base
  Dayton, Ohio 45433..........JAN

National Bureau of Standards
(Department of Commerce)
Washington, D. C. 20234........NBS

National Research Council of Canada
Division of Building Research
Ottawa, Ontario, Canada......NRCC

Naval Facilities Engineering
Command
(formerly Bureau of Yards and Docks)
Navy Department
Washington, D. C. 20390......NFEC

Navy Specifications
Bureau of Supplies and Accounts
Navy Department
Washington, D. C. 20225.........NS

Product Standards Section
Office of Engineering Standards
Services
National Bureau of Standards
Washington, D. C. 20234.........PS

Public Health Service
Department of Health, Education
and Welfare
Washington, D. C. 20201.......PHS

Superintendent of Documents
Government Printing Office
Washington, D. C. 20402.......GPO

United States Department of
Agriculture
Washington, D. C. 20225......USDA

United States Department of Commerce
Construction Division
Washington, D. C. 20225......USDC

United States Forest Service
Madison, Wisconsin 53705......USFS

United States Naval Supply Depot
5801 Tabor Avenue
Philadelphia, Pennsylvania 19120
......................USNSD

Interior Finishes and Masonry

Acoustical and Insulating Materials
Association
205 West Touhy Avenue
Park Ridge, Illinois 60068......AIMA

American Hardboard Association
20 North Wacker Drive
Chicago, Illinois 60606.........AHA

Asphalt and Vinyl Asbestos Tile
Institute
101 Park Avenue
New York, New York 10017...AVATI

Facing Tile Institute
333 North Michigan Avenue
Chicago, Illinois 60601..........FTI

Gypsum Association
201 North Wells Street
Chicago, Illinois 60606...........GA

Marble Institute of America, Inc.
Pennsylvania Building
Washington, D. C. 20004........MIA

195

Interior Finishes and Masonry—continued

Indiana Limestone Institute of
America, Inc.
400 East 7th Street-P.O. Box 489
Bloomington, Indiana 47401 . . . . . ILIA

National Building Granite Quarries
Association, Inc.
P.O. Box 444
Concord, New Hampshire 03302
. . . . NBGQA

National Concrete Masonry Association
2009 Fourteenth Street, North
Arlington, Virginia 22201 . . . . . NCMA

National Lime Association
4000 Brandywine Street, NW
Washington, D. C. 20016 . . . . . . NLA

National Particleboard Association
711 Fourteenth Street, NW
Washington, D. C. 20005 . . . . . . NPA

Perlite Institute, Inc.
45 West 45th Street
New York, New York 10036 . . . . PI

Portland Cement Association
5420 Old Orchard Road
Skokie, Illinois 60076 . . . . PCA

The Society of the Plastics
Industry, Inc.
250 Park Avenue
New York, New York 10017 . . . . . . SPI

Structural Clay Products Institute
1750 Old Meadow Road
McLean, Virginia 22101 . . . . SCPI

Tile Council of America
Research Center-P.O. Box 326
Princeton, New Jersey 08540 . . . . . TCA

Vermiculite Institute
208 South LaSalle Street
Chicago, Illinois 60604 VI

Metal and Steel

Aluminum Association
750 Third Avenue
New York, New York 10017 . . . . . . AA

American Institute of Steel
Construction, Inc.
101 Park Avenue
New York, New York 10017 . . . . . AISC

American Iron and Steel Institute
150 East 42nd Street
New York, New York 10017 . . . . . AISI

American Welding Society, Inc.
United Engineering Center
345 East 47th Street
New York, New York 10017 . . . . . AWS

Architectural Aluminum
Manufacturers Association
35 East Wacker Drive
Chicago, Illinois 60601 . . . . AAMA

Cast Iron Soil Pipe Institute
2029 K Street, NW
Washington, D. C. 20006 . . . . . . CISPI

Concrete Reinforcing Steel Institute
228 North LaSalle Street
Chicago, Illinois 60601 . . . . CRSI

Copper Development Association, Inc.
405 Lexington Avenue
New York, New York 10017 . . . . . CDA

Lead Industries Association, Inc.
292 Madison Avenue
New York, New York 10017 . . . . . . LIA

Metal Building Manufacturers
Association
2130 Keith Building
Cleveland, Ohio 44115 . . . . . . MBMA

Metal Lath Association
12703 Triskett
Cleveland, Ohio 44111 . . . . MLA

National Association of Architectural
Metal Manufacturers
228 North LaSalle Street
Chicago, Illinois 60601 . . . . . NAAMM

Rail Steel Bar Association
38 South Dearborn Street
Chicago, Illinois 60603 . . . . RSBA

Research Council on Riveted and
Bolted Structural Joints of the
Engineering Foundation
United Engineering Center
345 East 47th Street
New York, N. Y. 10017 . . . . RCRBSJEF

Steel Deck Institute
9836 W. Roosevelt Road
Westchester, Illinois 60153 . . . . SDI

Steel Bar Mills Association
(formerly Rail Steel Bar
Association)
38 South Dearborn Street
Chicago, Illinois 60603 . . . . SBMA

Steel Door Institute
2130 Keith Building
Cleveland, Ohio 44115 . . . . SDI

Steel Joist Institute
2001 Jefferson Davis Highway
Arlington, Virginia 22202 . . . . SJI

Steel Scaffolding & Shoring Institute
2130 Keith Building
Cleveland, Ohio 44115 . . . . SSSI

Metal and Steel—continued

The Steel Window Institute
2130 Kieth Building
Cleveland, Ohio 44115..........SWI

Wire Reinforcement Institute
5034 Wisconsin Avenue, NW
Washington, D. C. 20016........WRI

General Standards and Testing Laboratories

American Insurance Association
85 John Street
New York, New York 10038......AIA

American National Standards Institute,
Inc.
(formerly United States of America
Standards Institute, Inc.)
(formerly American Standards Association)
1430 Broadway
New York, New York 10018....ANSI

American Society for Testing and
Materials
P.O. Box 7510
Philadelphia, Pennsylvania
19101 ....ASTM

Factory Mutual Engineering Division
Standards-Laboratories Department
1151 Boston-Providence Turnpike
Norwood, Massachusetts 02062.FMED

National Fire Protection Association
60 Batterymarch Street
Boston, Massachusetts 02110...NFiPA

National Sanitation Foundation
Testing Laboratory, Inc.
School of Public Health
P. O. Box 1468
Ann Arbor, Michigan 48106...NSFTL

Underwriters' Laboratories, Inc.
207 East Ohio Street
Chicago, Illinois 60611..........ULI

Fire Testing Laboratories (Floor, Walls, Roof and Similar Tests)

National Bureau of Standards
(Department of Commerce)
Superintendent of Documents
Government Printing Office
Washington, D. C. 20234........NBS

The Ohio State University
Building Research Laboratory
2070 Neil Avenue
Columbus, Ohio 43210.........OSU

Underwriters' Laboratories, Inc.
207 East Ohio Street
Chicago, Illinois 60611..........ULI

Underwriters' Laboratories, Inc.
333 Pfingsten Road
Northbrook, Illinois 60062.......ULI

Underwriters' Laboratories, Inc.
1655 Scott Boulevard
Santa Clara, California 95050....ULI

University of California at Berkeley
College of Engineering
Berkeley, California 94720......UCB

Flamespread Testing Laboratories

Southwest Research Institute
8500 Culebra Road
San Antonio, Texas 78228......SWRI

Underwriters' Laboratories, Inc.
1655 Scott Boulevard
Santa Clara, California 95050....ULI

Underwriters' Laboratories, Inc.
333 Pfingsten Road
Northbrook, Illinois 60062.......ULI

Structural Testing Laboratories

The Detroit Testing Laboratory, Inc.
12800 Northend Avenue
Detroit, Michigan 48237........DTL

Forest Products Laboratory
United States Department
of Agriculture
Madison, Wisconsin 53705.......FPL

Robert W. Hunt Company
810 South Clinton
Chicago, Illinois 60607.........RWH

IIT Research Institute
(formerly Armour Research
Foundation)
10 West 35th Street
Chicago, Illinois 60616........IITRI

Structural Testing Laboratories—continued

NAHB Research Foundation, Inc.
Research Laboratory
Rockville, Maryland..........NAHB

H. C. Nutting Company
4120 Airport Road
Cincinnati, Ohio 45226.........HCN

The Ohio State University
Building Research Laboratory
2070 Neil Avenue
Columbus, Ohio 43210.........OSU

The Pennsylvania State University
Research Institute
University Park,
Pennsylvania 16802 ....PSU

Pittsburgh Testing Laboratory
1330 Locust Street
Pittsburgh, Pennsylvania 15219..PTL

University of Detroit
Research Institute
Detroit, Michigan 48221.........UD

Unclassified Miscellaneous

The American Institute of Architects
1735 New York Avenue, NW
Washington, D. C. 20006........AIA

American Public Health Association
1790 Broadway
New York, New York 10017....APHA

American Society of Civil Engineers
United Engineering Center
345 East 47th Street
New York, New York 10017....ASCE

American Society of Sanitary
Engineering
4328 South Western Avenue
Chicago, Illinois 60609........ASSE

American Water Works Association
2 Park Avenue
New York, New York 10016...AWWA

Building Officials Conference of
America, Inc.
1313 East 60th Street
Chicago, Illinois 60637........BOCA

Building Research Advisory Board
Division of Engineering
National Research Council
2101 Constitution Avenue
Washington, D. C. 20418......BRAB

Home Manufacturers Association
1625 L Street, NW
Washington, D. C. 20036.......HMA

International Association of Plumbing
& Mechanical Officials
5032 Alhambra Avenue
Los Angeles, California 90032.IAMPO

International Conference of Building
Officials
50 Souh Los Robles
Pasadena, California 91101.....ICBO

Manufacturing Chemists' Association,
Inc.
1825 Connecticut Avenue, NW
Washington, D. C. 20006......MCA

Mineral Fiber Products Bureau
509 Madison Avenue
New York, New York 10022....MFPB

Mobile Homes Manufacturers
Association
20 North Wacker Drive
Chicago, Illinois 60606.......MHMA

National Association of Home Builders
National Housing Center
1625 L Street, NW
Washington, D. C. 20036......NAHB

National Clay Pipe Institute
P.O. Box 310
350 West Terra Cotta Avenue
Crystal Lake, Illinois 60014.....NCPI

National Insulation Manufacturers
Association
441 Lexington Avenue
New York, New York 10017....NIMA

National Mineral Wool Insulation
Association
Rockefeller Center
1270 Sixth Avenue
New York, New York 10020..NMWIA

National Society of Professional
Engineers
2029 K Street, NW
Washington, D. C. 20006......NSPE

Southern Building Code Congress
750 Brown-Marx Building
Birmingham, Alabama 35203...SBCC

Truss Plate Institute, Inc.
Suite 800
919 Eighteenth Street, NW
Washington, D. C. 20006........TPI

Wood and Wood Products

Acoustical and Insulating Materials
Association
205 West Touhy Avenue
Park Ridge, Illinois 60068......AIMA

American Hardboard Association
20 North Wacker Drive
Chicago, Illinois 60606.........AHA

American Institute of Timber
Construction
1700 K Street, NW
Washington, D. C. 20006.......AITC

American Plywood Association
1119 A Street
Tacoma, Washington
98401 ....APA-DFPA

American Wood Preservers
Association
1012-14th Street, NW
Washington, D. C. 20037......AWPA

American Wood Preservers Institute
2600 Virginia Avenue, NW
Washington, D. C. 20005......AWPI

Appalachian Hardwood
Manufacturers, Inc.
1015 Mercantile Library Building
414 Walnut Street
Cincinnati, Ohio 45202.........AHM

Association of Timber and Timber
Treatment Inspection Agencies
729 Fisher Road
Grosse Pointe, Michigan
48230 ....ATTTIA

California Redwood Association
617 Montgomery Street
San Francisco, California 94111..CRA

Hardwood Plywood Manufacturers
Association
P.O. Box 6246
Arlington, Virginia 22206......HPMA

National Forest Products Association
1619 Massachusetts Avenue, NW
Washington, D. C. 20036.....NFoPA

National Particleboard Association
711 Fourteenth Street, NW
Washington, D. C. 20005.......NPA

Northeastern Lumber Manufacturers
Association, Inc.
271 Madison Avenue
New York, New York 10016...NLMA

Northern Hardwood and Pine
Manufacturers Association
207 Northern Building
Green Bay, Wisconsin
54301 ....NHPMA

Plywood Fabricator Service, Inc.
an affiliate of the American
Plywood Association
1119 A Street
Tacoma, Washington 98401......PFS

Red Cedar Shingle and Handsplit
Shake Bureau
5510 White Building
Seattle, Washington 98101...RCSHSB

Southern Hardwood Producers, Inc.
805 Sterick Building
Memphis, Tennessee 38103.....SHP

Southern Pine Association
National Bank of Commerce
Building
New Orleans, Louisiana 70112...SPA

Timber Engineering Company
1619 Massachusetts Ave., NW
Washington, D. C. 20036......TECO

Western Wood Products Association
700 Yeon Building
Portland, Oregon 97204......WWPA

APPENDIX C

DEFINITIONS ADOPTED BY MCSC, AUGUST 29, 1969

TERM	DEFINITION
Addition	Addition is an extension or increase in floor area or height of a building or structure.
Approved	Approved means approved by the building official or other authority having jurisdiction.
Apartment	The same definition as was adopted for dwelling unit.
Apartment House	An apartment house is a multiple dwelling for the purpose of providing three or more separate dwelling units with shared entrances and other essential facilities.
Area, Building	The building area is the maximum horizontally projected area of the building at or above grade, exclusive of court and vent shafts.
Area, Floor	The floor area is the usable area of each story of a building, or portion thereof, within surrounding exterior walls.
Automatic	Automatic, as applied to fire protection devices, is a device or system providing an emergency function without the necessity for human intervention and activated as a result of a predetermined temperature rise, rate of rise of temperature, or combustion products, such as an automatic sprinkler system, automatic fire door, automatic fire shutter, or automatic fire vent.
Basement	A basement is a story partially or fully below the grade plane.
Boiler	A boiler is a heating appliance intended to supply hot water or steam.
Building	A building is any structure used or intended for supporting or sheltering any use or occupancy.
Building, Existing	A building erected prior to the adoption of the appropriate code, or one for which a legal building permit has been issued.
Building Official	A Building Official is the officer or other designated authority charged with the administration and enforcement of this code, or his duly authorized representative.
Chimney Connector	A chimney connector is the pipe which connects a fuel burning appliance to a chimney.
Combustible Material	Combustible material is a material which cannot be classified as non-combustible in accordance with that definition.
Court	A court is an open, uncovered, and unoccupied space, other than a yard, on the same lot with a building.
Court, Inner	An inner court is any court other than an outer court.
Court, Outer	An outer court is a court extending to and opening upon a street, public alley, or other approved open space, not less than fifteen feet wide, or upon a required yard.

TERM	DEFINITION
Dormitory	A dormitory is a space in a residential unit where group sleeping accommodations are provided for persons not members of the same family group, in one room, or in a series of closely associated rooms under joint occupancy and single management, as in college dormitories, fraternity houses, military barracks, ski lodges; with or without meals.
Dwelling Unit	A dwelling unit is a residential unit providing complete, independent living facilities for one or more persons occupying a single unit, including permanent provisions for living, sleeping, eating, cooking, and sanitation.
Exit Access	An exit access is that portion of a means of egress which leads to an entrance to an exit.
Exit	Adopted—an exit is that portion of a means of egress which is separated from all other spaces of a building or structure by construction or equipment as required in this Code to provide a protected way of travel to the exit discharge.
Exit Discharge	Exit discharge is that portion of a means of egress between the termination of an exit and a public space.
Fire Doors	A fire door is a door and its assembly, so constructed and assembled in place as to give protection against the passage of fire.
Fire Partition	A fire partition is a wall to restrict the spread of fire in a fire area and with a fire resistive rating as required by the Code and with non-protected openings.
Fire Retardant	A property of a material or construction relating to flame spread characteristics.
Fire Separation Wall	A fire separation wall is a wall from floor to underside of floor or roof above, having a fire resistive rating as required by the Code, and subdividing areas of a building to resist the spread of fire, and has protected openings.
Fire Wall	A firewall is a wall which divides buildings or separated buildings to resist the spread of fire, and which starts at the foundation and extends continuously through all stories and in which openings must be protected by fire rated assemblies.
Flame Spread	Flame spread is the propagation of flame over a surface.
Flammable	Subject to easy ignition and rapid flaming combustion.
Grade	A grade is a reference plane representing the average of finished ground level adjoining the building at all exterior walls.
Habitable Space	Habitable space is space in a residential structure for living, sleeping, eating, or cooking. Bathrooms, toilet compartments, closets, halls, storage or utility space, and similar areas are not considered habitable space.
Hotel	A hotel is any building containing six or more guest rooms intended or designed to be used, or which are used, rented or hired out to be occupied or which are occupied for sleeping purposes by guests.
Lintel	A lintel is a beam placed over an opening or recess in a wall which supports the wall construction above.
Load, Dead	Dead load is the weight of all permanent structural and non-structural components of a building, such as walls, floors, roofs, and fixed service equipment.

201

TERM	DEFINITION
Load Duration	Load duration is the period of continuous application of a given load, or the aggregate of periods of intermittent applications of the same load.
Load, Live	A live load is the weight superimposed by the use and occupancy of the building, not including the wind load, earthquake load, or dead load.
Lodging House	A lodging house is any building or portion thereof containing not more than five guest rooms which are used by not more than five guests where rent is paid in money, goods, labor, or otherwise. A lodging house shall comply with all the requirements for dwellings.
Mezzanine	A mezzanine is an intermediate level between the floor and ceiling of any story, and covering less than 33⅓% of the floor area immediately beneath.
Means of Egress	A means of egress is a continuous and unobstructed way of exit travel from any point in a building or structure to a public space and consists of three separate and distinct parts: (a) the way of exit access, (b) the exit, and (c) the way of exit discharge. A means of egress comprises the vertical and horizontal ways of exit travel and shall include intervening room spaces, doors, hallways, corridors, passageways, balconies, ramps, stairs, enclosures, lobbies, escalators, horizontal exits, courts, and yards.
Motel	The same definition as was adopted for Hotel.
Occupancy	Occupancy is the purpose for which a building, or part thereof, is used or intended to be used.
Owner	An owner is any person, agent, firm, or corporation having a legal or equitable interest in the property.
Penthouse	A penthouse is an enclosed structure above the roof of a building, other than a roof structure or bulkhead, occupying not more than one-third of the roof area.
Permit	A permit is an official document or certificate issued by the authority having jurisdiction authorizing performance of a specified activity.
Plenum	A plenum is an air compartment or chamber to which one or more ducts are connected and which forms part of an air distribution system.
Preservative Treatment (Treated Material)	Preservative Treatment is, unless otherwise noted, impregnation under pressure with a wood preservative. Wood preservative is any suitable substance that is toxic to fungi, insects, borers, and other living wood-destroying organisms.
Public Space	Public space is a legal open space on the premises, accessible to a public way or street, such as yards, courts, or open spaces permanently dedicated to public use which abuts the premises.
Repair	Repair is the reconstruction or renewal of any part of an existing building for the purpose of its maintenance.
Roof Structure	A roof structure is an enclosed structure on or above the roof of any part of a building.
Self-closing	Self-closing, as applied to a fire door or other opening protective, means normally closed and equipped with an approved device which will insure closing after having been opened for use.

TERM	DEFINITION
Stage	A stage is a partially enclosed portion of an assembly building which is designed or used for the presentation of plays, demonstrations, or other entertainment wherein scenery, drops, or other effects may be installed or used, and where the distance between the top of the proscenium opening and the ceiling above the stage is more than five feet (5').
Story	A story is that portion of a building included between the upper surface of a floor and the upper surface of the floor or roof next above.
Story, First	The first story is the lowermost story entirely above the grade plane.
Street	A street is a public thoroughfare (street, avenue, boulevard) which has been dedicated for public use.
Structure	A structure is that which is built or constructed.
Vent System	A vent system is a continuous open passageway from the flue collar or draft hood of a fuel burning appliance to the outside atmosphere for the purpose of removing products of combustion.
Vertical Opening	A vertical opening is an opening through a floor or roof.
Wall, Bearing	A bearing wall is a wall supporting any vertical load in addition to its own weight.
Wall, Nonbearing	A nonbearing wall is a wall which supports no vertical load other than its own weight.
Wall, Retaining	A retaining wall is a wall designed to prevent the lateral displacement of soil or other material.
Written Notice	A written notice is a notification in writing delivered in person to the individual or parties intended, or delivered at, or sent by certified or registered mail to the last residential or business address of legal record.
Yard	A yard is an unoccupied open space other than a court.

APPENDIX D

OCCUPANCY CLASSIFICATIONS AS ADOPTED BY THE MODEL CODES STANDARDIZATION COUNCIL, AUGUST 29, 1969

Classification	Occupancy
A	Assembly
B	Business
E	Educational
F	Factory and Industrial
H	Hazardous
I	Institutional
M	Mercantile
R	Residential
S	Storage

APPENDIX E

ACCEPTED ENGINEERING PRACTICE STANDARDS

See also appendixes F, G, H, I, and J for standards on specific materials or tests of units or assemblies; some of which include engineering practice standards for specific applications.

High hazard materials handling and storage; fire protection
    devices; heating equipment rules; specifications and standards...................NFiPA
National Fire Codes; Handbook of Fire Protection; standards and reports......NFiPA
Technical bulletins of building construction data...HHFA

Concrete

Concrete Formwork—Recommended Practice for.................................ACI 347—68
Gypsum Concrete, Reinforced—Specifications for.........................USAS A 59.1—1968
Manufacture of Reinforced Concrete Floor and
    Roof Units—Recommended Practice for...ACI 512—67
Reinforced Concrete—Building Code Requirements for.....................ACI 318—1963
Reinforced Concrete Structures, Manual of Standard Practice
    for Detailing ....ACI 315—1965
Welding Reinforcing Steel, Metal Inserts and Connections
    in Reinforced Concrete Construction, Recommended
    Practices for ....AWS D 12.1—61

Electrical Illumination

Daylighting—Recommended Practices of..IES—1950
Electrical Code—National...NFiPA No. 70—1968
Electrical Safety Code—National...............................NBS Handbook H 30
Farmstead Wiring ....IES—1950
Home Lighting—Recommended Practice..IES—1953
Industrial Lighting ....ASA A 11.1—1952
Lighting Handbook ....IES—1952
Lighting Performance for Residence Luminaries............................IES—1946
Measuring Illumination in Buildings—Standard Method for.............IES—1948
Office Lighting—Recommended Practice..IES—1947
Residence Lighting—Recommended Practice......................................IES—1953
School Lighting—Recommended Practice..IES—1948
                               and AIA 31-F—1928
Wiring Handbook—Residential...IES—1947

Equipment

Air Conditioning and Ventilating

Air Conditioning and Ventilating Systems
    of Other Than Residence Type...NFiPA 90A—1968
Air Conditioning, Warm Air Heating and—
    Residence Type ....NFiPA 90B—1968
Blower and Exhaust Systems for Dust, Stock and Vapor
    Removal or Conveying...NFiPA 91—1961
Gas-Fired Absorption Summer Air Conditioning
    Appliances—USA Standard for.....................................ASA Z 21.40.1—1966

Equipment—continued

Heating, Warm Air, and Air Conditioning Systems,
Residence Type..*(See Air Conditioning Systems)*
Residence Type—Warm Air Heating and
Ventilating Systems...*(See Air Conditioning Systems)*
Warm Air Heating and Air Conditioning Systems,
Residence Type..*(See Air Conditioning Systems)*

Elevators and Lifts

Automotive Lifts..USDC CS 142–62
Elevators, Dumbwaiters, and Escalators—
Safety Code for..USAS A 17.1–1965
Supplement to Safety Code for Elevators, Dumbwaiters,
Escalators and Moving Walks.................................USAS A 17.1b–1968
Elevator Inspectors Manual...USAS A 17.2–1960
(with Supplements)..USAS A 17.2a–1960
USAS A 17.2b–1967
Manlifts—Safety Code for..ASA A 90.1–1949

Heating

Boiler Code and Unfired Pressure Vessel Code..............ASME—1965, 1966 & 1968
Chimneys, Fireplaces and Venting Systems—
Standard for ....NFiPA 211–1966
Central Heating Gas Appliances—Approved Requirements for
—Gas-Fired Gravity and Fan Type Floor Furnaces—
USA Standard for..ASA Z 21.48–1967
—Gas-Fired Gravity and Fan Type Vented Wall
Furnaces—USA Standard for....................................ASA Z 21.49–1967
—Gas Fired Gravity and Forced Air Central
Furnaces—USA Standard for....................................ASA Z 21.47–1968
—Gas-Fired Steam and Hot Water Boilers—
USA Standard for..ASA Z 21.13–1967
Gas-Fired Duct Furnaces—USA Standard for..................ASA Z 21.34–1968
Gas-Fired Room Heaters, Vol. 1, Vented Room Heaters—
USA Standard Approval Requirements for..................ASA Z 21.11.1–1965
Gas-Burning Equipment in Power Boilers—Requirements for
Installation of..ASA Z 21.33–1950
Gas-Fired Gravity and Fan Type Sealed Combustion
System Wall Furnaces—USA Standard for................ASA Z 21.44–1966
Gas-Fired Heavy Duty Forced Air Heaters—
USA Standard for..ASA Z 21.53–1967
Gas-Fired Single Firebox Boilers—USA Standard for..............ASA Z 21.52–1967
Gas Unit Heaters—USA Standard for................................ASA Z 21.16–1968
Unvented Gas-Fired Infrared Radiant Heaters—
USA Standard for..ASA Z 21.43–1968
Vented Gas-Fired Infrared Radiant Heaters—
USA Standard for..ASA Z 21.51–1967
Gravity Warm Air Heating Systems..ASHVE—1953
Heating, Ventilating and
Air Conditioning................................*(See Air Conditioning and Ventilating)*
High Pressure Boilers...ASME Boiler Code—1952
Low Pressure Boilers..HPACA Std.–1948
Oil Burners, Automatic Mechanical Draft Designed for
Domestic Installation...USDC CS 75–56
Oil Burning Equipment...NFiPA 31–1968
Oil Burning Floor Furnaces Equipped with Vaporizing
Pot Type Burners..USDC CS 113–63
Residence Type—Warm Air Heating and
Air Conditioning Systems...................*(See Air Conditioning and Ventilating)*
Solid Fuel Burning Forced Air Furnaces....................USDC CS 109–47
Warm Air Heating and
Air Conditioning Systems...................*(See Air Conditioning and Ventilating)*

Incinerators

Domestic Gas-Fired Incinerators—USA Standard
Approval Requirements for...ASA Z 21.6–1966
Incinerator Standards...IIA—April 1963

Equipment—continued

Plumbing and Piping (Gas or Water)

Air Gaps in Plumbing Systems for Plumbing Fixtures
and All Water-Connected Devices..USAS A40.4–1942
Backflow Preventers in Plumbing Systems (Vacuum Breakers)
for Plumbing Fixtures and All Water-Connected Devices........USAS A40.6–1943
Gas Piping and Gas Appliances—Installation of............................ASA Z 21.30–1964
Gas Piping in Buildings, Gas Appliances and—Installation of............NFiPA 54–1964
Gas Piping and Gas Equipment on Industrial Premises
and Certain Other Premises—USA Standard Installation of......ASA Z 83.1–1968
Gas Water Heaters, Volume 1, Automatic Storage Type
Water Heaters with Inputs Less Than 50,000 BTU
Per Hour—Approval Requirements for....................................USAS Z21.10.1–1966
Gas Water Heaters, Volume III, Circulating Tank,
Instantaneous and Large Automatic Storage Type
Water Heaters—Approval Requirements for............................USAS Z21.10.3–1966
National Plumbing Code...ASA A40.8–1955
Pipe Applied Atmospheric Type Vacuum Breakers—
Standards and Test Procedures for..ASSE 1001–May, 1966
Relief Valves and Automatic Gas Shutoff Devices for
Hot Water Supply Systems—Listing Requirements for............USAS Z21.22–1964
Water Pressure Reducing Valves for
Domestic Water Supply Systems—Self-Contained,
Direct-Acting, Single Seat, Diaphragm Type........................ASSE 1003–Oct., 1964

Refrigeration

Mechanical Refrigeration—Safety Code for....................................ASHREA 15–1964
Also ASA B 9.1–1964

Unclassified—Miscellaneous

Mobile Home Standards for Plumbing, Heating, and
Electrical Systems...MHMA–1959
Swimming Pools and Other Public Bathing Places, Equipment
and Operation—Recommended Practice for Design.....................APHA–1949
Travel Trailer Standards for Electrical, Plumbing, Heating
and LP-Gas Consuming Appliances Systems.................................MHMA–1960

Fire Protection and Safety Practices

Safety to Life from Fire in Buildings and Structures......................NFiPA 101–1967
   NOTE: *NFiPA 101–1967 is acceptable for matters of design of exits
   not provided for by the BOCA Codes. Finish and construc-
   tion requirements incorporated therein are not applicable.*
Aircraft Hangars...NFiPA 409–1967
Cutting and Welding—Oxygen Fuel Gas
Systems for ....NFiPA 51–1964
Dry Cleaning and Dry Dyeing Plants..NFiPA 32–1964
Dust Explosions and Ignition
—in Country Grain Elevators—Prevention of.....................................NFiPA 64–1959
—in Flour and Feed Mills and Allied Grain Storage
Elevators—Prevention of ....NFiPA 61C–1962
—in Industrial Plants—Fundamental Principles
for the Prevention of..NFiPA 63–1964
—Pulverized Fuel Systems—Installation and Operation of................NFiPA 60–1961
—in Starch Factories—Prevention of..NFiPA 61A–1962
—in Terminal Grain Elevators—Prevention of Dust Explosions......NFiPA 61B–1959
Film, Motion Picture, Cellulose Nitrate—
Storing and Handling of..NFiPA 40–1967
Garages ....NFiPA 88–1968
Gases, Liquefied Petroleum—Storage and Handling of.....................NFiPA 58–1965
Gas, Liquefied Petroleum at Utility Gas Plants—
Storage and Handling of...NFiPA 59–1968
Heating, Ventilating and Air Conditioning............................*(See Equipment—Heating)*

Fire Protection and Safety Practices—continued

Glass

Interior Finishes

Masonry

Metals

Aluminum Construction Manual, Specifications for
Aluminum Structures ....AA—1967

Steel

Design of Cold-Formed Steel Structural Members—
Specification for...AISI—1968

Design, Fabrication and Erection of Structural Steel for
Buildings—Specification for..AISC—1969

Design of Light Gage Cold-Formed Stainless Steel Structural
Members—Specification for...AISI—1968

Open Web Steel Joists, J-Series and H-Series—
Standard Specification for...SJI/AISC—1965

Longspan Steel Joists, LJ-Series and LH-Series—
Standard Specification for...AISC/SJI—1966

Welding in Building Construction—
Code for...AWS D 1.0—69

Structural Applications of Steel Cables for Buildings—
Tentative Criteria for..AISI—1966

Structural Joints Using ASTM A325 or A490 Bolts—
Specification for...AISC—1966

Architecturally Exposed Structural Steel—
Specification for...AISC—1960

Gas Systems for Welding and Cutting........*(See Fire Protection and Safety Practices)*

Design Practices Manual, Recommended..MBMA—1967

Wood and Wood Products

Hurricane-Resistant Plywood Construction...APA—1966

Maximum Spans for Joists and Rafters in
Residential Construction ....NFoPA—1961 incl. 1962 Supplement

Pile Building Design ....AWPI—1969

Pile Foundations Know How...AWPI—1968

Plywood Beams—Design and Fabrication of..APA—1966

Plywood Construction Systems..APA—1967

Plywood Curven Panels—Design and Fabrication of..APA—1964

Plywood Design Specifications...APA—1966

Plywood Folded Plate Fabrication..APA—1966

Plywood Stressed Skin Panels—Design and Fabrication of.................................APA—1964

Pressure Treated Timber Foundation Piles for
Permanent Structures..AWPI—1965

Pressure Treated Timber Piles for Permanent Structures.......................AWPI—1967

Simplified Span Tables for Joists and Rafters
in Residential Construction...NFoPA—1966

Stress Grade Lumber and Its Fastenings—National Design
Specifications for ....NFoPA—1968

Structural Design Data—Wood..NFoPA—1967

Timber Construction Manual...AITC—1966

Timber Construction Standards..AITC—100—1969

Timber Structural Glued Laminated—
Inspection Manual for................................AITC 200—63 with 1967 Supplement

Wood Handbook..USDA Handbook No. 72—1955

209

Unclassified-Miscellaneous

Building Codes—Administrative Requirements for..........................ASA A 55.1—1948
Building Construction—Safety Code for..ASA A 10.2—1944
Building Materials—Coordination of Dimensions of......................ASA A 62.1—1957
Clay Flue Linings—Sizes of..ASTM C 315—63
Fallout Shelters—Suggested Building Code
   Provision for ....DOD-OCD TR-36—1966
Fibrous Glass Air Duct—Standard for..NIMA Feb. 1, 1965
Floor and Wall Openings,
   Railings, and Tow Boards—Safety Code for................................ASA A 12—1932
Floors—Waterproofing of ....NFiPA 92—1937
Homes—Prefabricated ....USDC CS 125—1947
Installing Vitrified Clay Sewer Pipe..ASTM C 12—64
Light and Ventilation—Standards for..ASA A 53.1—1946
Loads, Minimum Design—Standards for..ASA A 58.1—1955
Safety Code for Vertical Shoring—Recommended Standard............................SSSI—68
Signs and Outdoor Display Structures—Standards for........................ASA 60.1—1949

APPENDIX F

MATERIAL STANDARDS

See also Appendix G for standards for tests of specific materials.

Concrete

Aggregates, Concrete Specifications for..ASTM C 33–67
Aggregates, Lightweight, for Structural Concrete—
  Specifications for...ASTM C 330–64T
Aggregates, Lightweight, for Concrete Masonry Units.........................(*See Masonry*)
Aggregates, Lightweight, for Insulating Concrete—
  Specifications for ....ASTM C 332–66
Bar Supports, Wire, in Reinforced Concrete Construction—
  Simplified Practice Recommendations for..............................USDC SP 4687
Forms for Concrete Joist Construction Floors.............................USDC R 87–32
Forms for Two-Way Concrete Joist Floor and
  Roof Construction..USDC R 265–63
Gypsum Concrete—Specifications for..ASTM C 317–64
Manufacture of Reinforced Concrete Floor and
  Roof Units—Recommended practice for................................ACI 512–67
Masonry Units—Concrete ....(*See Masonry*)
Natural Cement—Specifications for..ASTM C 10–64
Portland Cement, Air-Entraining—Specifications for....................ASTM C 175–67
Portland Cement—Specifications for..ASTM C 150–67
Ready Mix Concrete—Specifications for.....................................ASTM C 94–67
Reinforcing ....(*See Metals*)
Roofs and Slabs-On-Grade, Vermiculite Concrete—
  Specifications for...ASA A 122.1–1965
Waterproof Paper for Curing Concrete—Specifications for............ASTM C 171–63

Fire Protection

Fire Retardant Properties of Treated Textile Fabrics—
  Specifications for...ASTM D 626–55T

Interior Finishes

Adhesives, Organic, for Installation of
  Ceramic Tile—Standard for..USAS A 136.1–67
Adhesive—Water Resistant Organic, for Installation of
  Clay Tile ....USDC CS 181–52
Aggregates, Inorganic, for use in Gypsum Plaster—
  Specifications for...ASTM C 35–67
Dry-Set Portland Cement Mortar—
  (for Ceramic Tile)..(*See Masonry*)
Gypsum and Gypsum Products, Chemical Analysis of—
  Standard Methods for..ASTM C 471–66
Gypsum Base for Veneer Plaster—Specifications for....................ASTM C 588–66T
Gypsum Board Products and Gypsum Partition Tile or Block,
  Physical Testing of—Standard Methods for...........................ASTM C 473–66
Gypsum Lath—Specifications for..ASTM C 37–67
Gypsum Plasters—Specifications for..ASTM C 28–66
Gypsum Plasters and Gypsum Concrete, Physical Testing of—
  Standard Methods for..ASTM C 472–66

Interior Finishes—continued

Masonry

Metal

Metal—continued

Codes and Code Administration

Metal—continued

Plumbing and Piping

Plumbing and Piping—continued

Cast Iron Pipe
—Pressure—Specifications for..ASTM A 377—57
—Soil Pipe and Fittings—Specifications for..................................ASTM A 74—66
Clay Pipe
—Compression Joints ....ASTM C 425—66T
—Drain Tile—Specifications for..ASTM C 4—62
—Extra Strength—Specifications for..ASTM C 200—65T
—Perforated ....ASTM C 211—68
—Sewer, Standard Strength Ceramic Glazed or Unglazed—
   Specifications for..ASTM C 261—60T
—Sewer, Standard Strength—Specifications for............................ASTM C 13—65T
Concrete Pipe
—Culvert Storm Drain and Sewer, Reinforced—
   Specifications for..ASTM C 76—64T
—Sewer—Specifications for..ASTM C 14—63
Copper Drainage Tube (DWV)...ASTM B 306—62
Copper Pipe
—Seamless, Standard Sizes—Specifications for............................ASTM B 42—62
Fiber Pipe, Bituminized Drain and Sewer..USDC CS 116—54
Lead Pipe..FS WW-P-325
Non-Metallic Pipe and Fittings..USDC CS 255—63 (ABS)
Plastic Drain, Waste and Vent Pipe and Fittings—
   Acrylonitrile Butadiene-Styrene (ABS)..............................USDC CS 270—65
Plastic Drain, Waste and Vent Pipe and Fittings—
   Polyvinyl Chloride (PVC)..USDC CS 272—65
Plastic Pipe and Fittings..USDC CS 255—63 (PE)
   (Water Supply) ....USDC CS 256—63 (PVC)
Sewer and Storm Drain..USDC CS 228—61 (SRP)
Steel Pipe
—Black and Hot Dipped Zinc Coated (Galvanized) Welded
   and Seamless, for Ordinary Uses—Specifications for....................ASTM A 120—65
—Steel or Iron, Special—Welded—Specifications for........................ASTM A 211—63
—Welded and Seamless—Specifications for....................................ASTM A 53—69
Tile, Clay Drain..*(See Clay Pipe)*
Traps and Bends, Lead..FS WW-P-325
Tube and Tubing
—Brass, Seamless—Specifications for..ASTM B 135—63
—Copper, Seamless—Specifications for..ASTM B 75—66
—Copper, Seamless, Water—Specifications for................................ASTM B 88—62
—Copper Brazed Steel Tubing—Specifications for........................ASTM A 254—64
Wrought Iron and Wrought Steel Pipe..ASA B 36.10—59
Wrought Iron Pipe, Welded—Specifications for............................ASTM A 72—66
Valves, Flanges and Pipe Fittings, Gray Iron Castings—
   Specifications for ....ASTM A 126—61T

Roofing and Siding

Asphalt for Dampproofing and Waterproofing—
   Specifications for ....ASTM D 449—49
Asphalt for Use in Constructing Built-Up Roof Coverings—
   Specifications for ....ASTM D 312—64
Asphalt Roll Roofing Surfaced with Mineral Granules—
   Specifications for ....ASTM D 249—60
Asphalt Roll Roofing Surfaced with Powdered Talc or Mica—
   Specifications for ....ASTM D 224—58
Asphalt-Saturated and Coated Asbestos Felts for Use in
   Constructing Built-Up Roofs—Specifications for....................ASTM D 655—47
Asphalt Shingles Surfaced with Mineral Granules—
   Specifications for ....ASTM D 225—62
Asphalt Siding Surfaced with Mineral Granules—
   Specifications for ....ASTM D 699—58
Fiberboard Nail-Base Sheathing—Standard
   Specification for ....ASTM D 2277—66

Roofing and Siding—continued

Wood and Wood Products

Unclassified Miscellaneous

Felt—Methods of Testing..ASTM D 461–61
Fire Retardant Plastics for Roofing and Siding.....................FMED Standard 4420
Fire-Retardant Properties of Treated Textile Fabrics—
   Specifications for ....ASTM D 626–55T
Flammability of Plastics 0.050 inches and Under in
   Thickness—Method of Test for..ASTM D 568–61
Flammability of Rigid Plastics Over 0.050 inches in
   Thickness—Method of Test for......................... ....ASTM D 635–63
Formboard, Gypsum—Specifications for..............................ASTM C 318–55
Insulated Metal Roof Deck Standard...................................FMED Standard 4450
Mineral Wool Building Insulation—Standard for.................NMWIA–60
Perlite Loose Fill Insulation—Standard Specifications for.............ASTM C 549–67
Plastics—Definitions of Terms Relating to............................ASTM D 883–64aT
Plastics, Deformation of, Under Load—Method of Test for...........ASTM D 621–64
Preservatives for Wood
  —Creosote—Standards for...AWPA P 1–65
  —Creosote, Coal Tar Solutions—Standards for.................AWPA P 2–68
  —Oil-Borne Preservatives—Standards for.......................AWPA P 8–68
  —Oil-Borne Solvents—Standards for...............................AWPA P 9–67
  —Water-Borne Preservatives—Standards for....................AWPA P 5–68
Thickness of Solid Electrical Insulation—Method of Test for.......ASTM D 374–57T
Vermiculite Loose Fill Insulation—Standard Specifications for.......ASTM C 516–67
Waterproof Paper for Curing Concrete—Specifications for...........ASTM D 374–57T
Waterproof Paper for Curing Concrete—Specifications for..................(*See Concrete*)
Zinc Chromate Primer..U.S.N. Dept. Spec. 52-18

APPENDIX G

STRUCTURAL UNIT TEST STANDARDS

See also appendixes E and F for engineering practice standards and material standards which contain unit test methods.

Concrete

Coarse Aggregates, Resistance to Abrasion of Small Size, by use of the Los Angeles Abrasion Machine—Test for	ASTM C 131—66
Fine and Coarse Aggregates, Sieve or Screen Analysis of— Test for (A 37.8—1967)	ASTM C 136—67
Graded Coarse Aggregates, Abrasion of, by Use of the Deval Machine—Method of Test for	ASTM D 289—63
Concrete, Securing, Preparing, and Testing Specimens from Hardened, for Compressive and Flexural Strength (A 37.20—1966)	ASTM C 42—64
Concrete Compression and Flexure Test Specimens in the Laboratory—Making and Curing	ASTM C 192—66
Concrete, Molded Cylinders—Test for Compressive Strength of	ASTM C 39—66
Lightweight Insulating Concrete, Compressive Strength—Test for	ASTM C 495—66
Concrete Masonry Units—Sampling and Testing (A 84.1—1967)	ASTM C 140—65T
Concrete Masonry Units, Hollow Load Bearing— Specifications for	ASTM C 90—66T
Concrete, Masonry Units, Solid Load Bearing— Specifications for (A 81.1—1967)	ASTM C 145—66T
Concrete, Hardened Portland Cement—Test for Cement Content of (A 1.22—1967)	ASTM C 85—66
Concrete, Ready Mixed—Specifications for (A 37.69—1967)	ASTM C 94—67
Sands for Concrete—Test for Organic Impurities in	ASTM C 40—66

Interior Finishes

Ceramic Tile, Method of Test for Bond Strength of, to Portland Cement Mortar	ASTM C 452—64T
Gypsum and Gypsum Products, Chemical Analysis of— Standard Methods for	ASTM C 471—66
Gypsum Board Products and Gypsum Partition Tile or Block, Physical Testing of—Standard Methods for	ASTM C 473—66
Gypsum Concrete—Specifications for	ASTM C 317—64
Gypsum Formload—Specifications for	ASTM C 318—67
Gypsum Lath—Specifications for	ASTM C 37—67
Gypsum Plasters—Specifications for	ASTM C 28—67
Gypsum Plasters and Gypsum Concrete, Physical Testing of— Standard Methods for	ASTM C 472—66
Gypsum Sheathing Board—Specifications for	ASTM C 79—67
Gypsum Wallboard—Specifications for	ASTM C 36—67
Insulation Board, Structural, Made from Vegetable Fibers— Methods of Testing	ASTM C 209—66
Specifications for	ASTM C 208—66
Lime	(See **Masonry**)

Masonry

Aggregate for Masonry Mortar—Specifications for.........................ASTM C 144–66T
Brick, Concrete Building—Specifications for............................ASTM C 55–66T
Brick—Methods of Testing and Sampling.............................ASTM C 67–66
Cement, Masonry—Specifications for.............................ASTM C 91–67
Ceramic Tile (Veneers)...(See Interior Finishes)
Chemical Analysis of Limestone, Quicklime and
    Hydrated Lime ....ASTM C 25–67
Concrete Masonry Units...(See Concrete)
Glazed Units—Ceramic Glazed Structural Clay Facing Tile,
    Facing Bricks, and Solid Masonry Units—Specifications for........ASTM C 126–67
Lime and Limestone Products—Methods of Sampling,
    Inspection, Packing and Marking of...............................ASTM C 50–57
Lime, Hydrated and Quick—Methods of Physical Testing of.........ASTM C 110–67
Lime, Hydraulic Hydrated for Structural Purposes—
    Specifications for ....ASTM C 141–67
Mortars, Hydraulic Cement—Method of Test for
    Compressive Strength of (Using 2 in. cube Specimens).............ASTM C 109–64
Mortars, Hydraulic Cement—Method of Test
    for Tensile Strength of...ASTM C 190–63
Stone, Natural Building—Methods of Test for
    Absorption and Bulk Specific Gravity of.........................ASTM C 97–58
Stone, Natural Building—Method of Test for
    Compressive Strength of..ASTM C 170–58
Stone, Natural Building—Methods of Test for
    Modulus of Ruptures of..ASTM C 99–58
Tile, Structural Clay—Methods of Sampling and Testing.............ASTM C 112–60

Metals

Cast Iron—Method of Testing Compression of.........................ASTM A 256–46
Metallic Materials—Methods of Tension Testing of...................ASTM E 8–61T

Unclassified Miscellaneous

Cement, Hydraulic—Methods of Sampling...............................ASTM C 183–65T
Cement, Natural—Specifications for.......................................ASTM C 10–64
Cement, Portland—Specifications for.....................................ASTM C 150–68
Clay Pipe, Testing...ASTM C 301–68
Plastics Under Load—Method of Test for Deformation of..............ASTM D 621–64
Tile, Clay Drain—Specification for.......................................ASTM C 4–62

Wood and Wood Products

Evaluating the Properties of Wood-Base Fiber
    and Particle Panel Materials......................................ASTM D 1037–64
Timber, Small Clear Specimens—Method of Testing...................ASTM D 143–52
Timbers in Structural Sizes—Methods of Static Tests of.............ASTM D 198–67
Veneer, Plywood and Other Glazed Veneer Construction—
    Methods of Testing..ASTM D 805–63

APPENDIX H

STRUCTURAL ASSEMBLY TEST STANDARDS

See also appendix G for standards for tests of unit materials.

APPENDIX I

DURABILITY TEST STANDARDS

See also appendixes F, G and H for tests of individual materials or unit assemblies.

Concrete and Concrete Aggregate

Concrete, Aggregate—Method of Tests for Voids in	ASTM C 30–37
Concrete, Air Content of Freshly Mixed, by the Pressure Method—Method of Test for	ASTM C 231–62
Concrete, Weight per Cubic Foot, Yield and Air Content of—Method of Test for	ASTM C 138–63
Organic Impurities in Sand for Concrete—Method of Test for	ASTM C 40–66

Masonry and Masonry Products

Ceramic Glazed Structural Clay Facing Tile, Facing Brick and Solid Masonry Units—Specifications for (Autoclave Test)	ASTM C 126–67
Freezing and Thawing Tests (See Specifications for Materials)	
—Bricks—Methods of Sampling and Testing	ASTM C 67–66
—Drain Tile—Specifications for	ASTM C 4–62
—Structural Clay Tile—Methods of Sampling and Testing	ASTM C 112–60

Plastics

Accelerated Weathering Tests of Plastics—Recommended Practice for	ASTM D 795–57T
Water Absorption of Plastics—Method of Test for	ASTM D 570–63

Roofing and Siding

Asphalt Roll Roofing, Cap Sheets, and Shingles—Methods of Testing	ASTM D 228–64
Bituminous Materials, Accelerated Test of Weathering—Recommended Practice for	ASTM D 529–62
Felted and Woven Fabrics Saturated with Bituminous Substance for Use in Waterproofing and Roofing—Methods of Sampling and Testing	ASTM D 146–59

Unclassified Miscellaneous

Fibre Building Boards—Method of Accelerated Aging	NBS BMS 4–38
Fibre Building Boards—Method of Accelerated Aging	ASTM D 1037–63T
Gypsum and Gypsum Products, Chemical Analysis of—Standard Methods for	ASTM C 471–61
Gypsum Board Products and Gypsum Partition Tile or Block, Physical Testing of—Standard Methods of	ASTM C 473–62
Gypsum Plasters and Gypsum Concrete, Physical Testing of—Standard Methods for	ASTM C 472–64
Textile Fabrics—Method of Test for Water Resistance of	ASTM D 583–63

APPENDIX J

FIRE TEST AND FLAME SPREAD TEST STANDARDS

Combustible or Noncombustible Properties

Fire-Retardant Treatments of Building Materials..............................NFPA 703–1961
Noncombustibility of Elementary Materials—
　Method of Test for Determining...ASTM E 136–65
Textile Fabrics, Treated—Specifications for
　Fire-Retardant Properties of..ASTM D 626–55T
Wood, Treated—Method of Test for Combustible Properties of
—by the Crib Test...ASTM E 160–50
—by the Fire Tube Apparatus...ASTM E 69–50

Fire Resistance Properties

Building Construction and Materials—Methods of
　Fire Test of..ASTM E 119–67
Ceiling Construction—(See Building Construction)
Door Assemblies—Methods of Fire Tests of......................................ASTM E 152–66
Roof Coverings—Methods of Fire Test of...ASTM E 108–58

Flame Spread Properties

Flame Resistance Tests—Acoustical Units,
　Prefabricated..Fed. Spec. SSA 00118c–60
Surface Burning Characteristics of Building Materials—
　Method of Test for...ASTM E 84–68

Flash Point

Fuel Oils, by Pensky-Masters Closed Tester—
　Method of Test for Flash Point..ASTM D 93–62
Liquids other than Fuel Oil, by Tag Closed Tester—
　Method of Test for Flash Point..ASTM D 56–64
Flash and Fire Points by Cleveland Open Cup—
　Method of Test for..ASTM D 92–57

APPENDIX K

FIRE PROTECTION STANDARDS

Alarm and Detecting Systems

Alarm Systems, Municipal—Installations, Maintenance
and Use of..NFiPA 73—1967
Signaling Systems, Central Station Protective—
For Watchman, Fire Alarm and Supervisory Service,
Installation, Maintenance and Use of................................NFiPA 71—1967
Signaling Systems, Proprietary, Auxiliary and Local
Protective—Installation, Maintenance and Use of..............NFiPA 72—1964
Signaling Systems—Installation, Maintenance and Use
Local Protective..NFiPA 72A—1967
Auxiliary Protective...NFiPA 72B—1967
Remote Station Protective..NFiPA 72C—1967
Proprietary Protective..NFiPA 72D—1967

Prevention of Spread of Fire

Air Conditioning and Ventilating Systems
—other than Residence Type...NFiPA 90A—1966
—Residence Type ....NFiPA 90B—1965
Aircraft Hangars ....NFiPA 409—1967
Doors, Tin-Clad Fire...ULI 10a—56
Dust Explosion Prevention..(See App. B)
Fire Doors and Windows—Standard for..............................NFiPA 80—1968
Hardware, Sliding, for Standard Tin-Clad Fire Doors.............ULI 14(b) Nov. 1953
Hardware, Swinging, for Standard Tin-Clad Fire Doors..........ULI 14(c)—1968
Prevention and Spread of Fire Approved Fire Protection
Equipment and Building Materials.....................................FMED

Protection Systems

Carbon Dioxide Extinguishing Systems.............................NFiPA 12—1968
Extinguishers, Portable Fire—Installation.........................NFiPA 10A—1968
Extinguishers, Portable Fire, Maintenance and Use...........NFiPA 10B—1968
Foam Extinguishing Systems..NFiPA 11—1963
Foam-Water Sprinkler and Foam-Water Spray Systems.......NFiPA 16—1968
Hose Systems..(See Standpipe
and Hose Systems)
Outside Protection (Yard Mains for Sprinklers, Standpipes, etc.)......NFiPA 24—1968
Private Fire Brigades—Organization, Training and Equipment of....NFiPA 27—1967
Pumps, Centrifugal Fire—Installation of............................NFiPA 20—1968
Sprinkler Systems
—Installation of ....NFiPA 13—1968
—Care and Maintenance of..NFiPA 13A—1968
Standpipe and Hose Systems...NFiPA 14—1968
Valves Controlling Water Supplies for Fire Protection—
Supervision of ....NFiPA 26—58
Water Tanks for Private Fire Protection.............................NFiPA 22—1967
Water Spray Systems..NFiPA 15—1962

APPENDIX L

UNIT DESIGN DEAD LOADS
FOR STRUCTURAL DESIGN PURPOSES

Walls and Partitions (Unplastered)

	Pounds per Square Foot
12 inch common brick	120
12 " pressed brick	130
12 " sand-lime brick	105
12 " hollow concrete block—Stone Aggregate	74
Lightweight	55
10 " hollow concrete block—Stone Aggregate	62
Lightweight	46
8 " hollow concrete block—Stone Aggregate	50
Lightweight	36
6 " hollow concrete block—Stone Aggregate	42
Lightweight	36
4 " hollow concrete block—Stone Aggregate	27
Lightweight	20
12 " solid concrete block—Stone Aggregate	108
Lightweight	72
10 " solid concrete block—Stone Aggregate	84
Lightweight	62
8 " solid concrete block—Stone Aggregate	67
Lightweight	48
6 " solid concrete block—Stone Aggregate	50
Lightweight	37
4 " solid concrete block—Stone Aggregate	45
Lightweight	34
12 " combination brick and clay tile	80
8 " " " " " "	60
12 " combination brick and concrete block	90
8 " " " " "	72
12 inch load-bearing clay tile	60
8 " " " " " "	40
6 " " " " " "	36
4 " " " " " "	24
10 " non-load-bearing clay tile	40
8 " " " " " "	36
6 " " " " " "	30
4 " " " " " "	20
3 " " " " " "	18
2 " " " " " "	11
8 " non-load-bearing hollow concrete block	40
6 " " " " " " "	30
4 " " " " " " "	20
T.C. 1½ inch split terra cotta furring	8
2 inch split terra cotta furring	10
3 " " " " "	12
6 " hollow gypsum block	24
5 " " " " "	18
4 " " " " "	15
3 " " " " "	10

	Pounds per Square Foot
4 inch solid gypsum block	24
3 " " " "	18
2 " " " "	12
4 " glass block	18

	Pounds per Cubic Foot
Cast stone solid	144
Granite ashlar	168
Limestone ashlar	168
Marble ashlar	168
Sandstone ashlar	156
Rubble stone masonry	156
Terra cotta architectural (filled)	120
Terra cotta architectural (unfilled)	72
Concrete, stone (plain)	144
Concrete, stone (reinforced)	150
Concrete, cinder	108
Fill, cinder	60
Earth (dry)	96
Earth (damp)	108
Earth (wet)	120
Cork	15
Timber, Ash	40
Timber, Douglas Fir	36
Timber, Cypress	30
Timber, Hemlock	30
Timber, Oak	48
Southern Pine, Short Leaf	36
Southern Pine, Long Leaf	48
Redwood	28
Spruce	30

Plaster Work

Pounds per Square Foot

Gypsum (one side)	5
Cement (one side)	10
Gypsum on wood lath	8
Gypsum on metal lath	8
Gypsum on plaster board or fiber board	8
Cement on wood lath	10
Cement on metal lath	10

Suspended Ceilings

Pounds per Square Foot

Cement on wood lath	12
Cement on metal lath	15
Gypsum on wood or metal lath	10

Lath and Plaster Partitions

Pounds per Square Foot

2 inch solid cement on metal lath	25
2 " solid gypsum on metal lath	18
2 " " " on gypsum lath	18
2 " metal studs gypsum & metal lath both sides	18
3 " " " " " " " "	19
4 " " " " " " "	20
6 inch wood studs plaster and wood lath, both sides	18
6 " " " " " metal lath, both sides	18
6 " " " " " plaster boards, both sides	18
6 " " " unplastered gypsum board, both sides (dry wall)	10

225

Floor and Roof Construction

Pounds per Square Foot

Cinder fill per inch depth	5
Cinder concrete per inch depth	9
Stone concrete per inch depth	12
Floor finish tile per inch depth	12
Cement finish per inch depth	12
Gypsum slabs per inch depth	4
Precast concrete plank per inch depth (as determined by test)	
Hardwood flooring per inch depth	4
Underflooring per inch depth	3
Linoleum	2
Asphalt tile	2

Roofs and Roofing

Pounds per Square Foot

Metal Skylights	10
3-ply roofing	4
4 " "	5
5 " "	6
Wood sheathing (1")	3
Plywood sheathing (5⁄16")	1
Corrugated iron roofing	3
Formed steel decking	3
Sheet lead	3
Slate tile roofing	10
Cement tile	16
Spanish tile	20
Shingles, asbestos	6
Shingles, asphalt	6
Shingles, wood	6

APPENDIX M

MINIMUM UNIFORMLY DISTRIBUTED LIVE LOADS

Use	Pounds per square foot
Alleys, driveways, yards and terraces	
Pedestrian	100
Vehicular	250
Armories and drill rooms	150
Assembly:	
Fixed seats	60
Removable or no seats	100
Balcony (exterior)	100
Bowling alleys, pool rooms and similar recreational areas	75
Class Rooms	
Schools, colleges and Sunday schools	40(d)
Cornices	75
Corridors and hallways	
Hotels, hospitals and multi-family dwellings	60
One- and two-family dwellings	40
Serving public rooms in hotels	100
Corridors and entrance hallways other than residential buildings	100
Corridors (other than those specifically designated):	
Private	Same as occupancy served

APPENDIX N

CONCENTRATED LOADS

Location	Pounds
Elevator machine room grating (on area of 4 sq. in.)	300
Finish light floor plate construction (on area of 1 sq. in.)	200
Garages, and parking structures for passenger cars	2000
Garages, trucks (not less than 150 per cent maximum wheel load)	—
Office floors	2000
Parking structures for passenger cars	2000
Scuttles and skylight ribs	200
Sidewalks	8000
Stair treads (on center of tread)	300

APPENDIX O

UNDERWRITERS' LABORATORIES BACKGROUND

Underwriters' Laboratories, Inc., "UL", was founded in 1894 by William Henry Merrill. After coming to Chicago to test the installation of Thomas Edison's new incandescent electric light at the Columbian Exposition, he started "UL" for insurance companies to test products for electric and fire hazards. It continued as a testing laboratory for insurance underwriters until 1917, when it became an independent, self-supporting safety testing laboratory. The National Board of Fire Underwriters (now American Insurance Association) continued as sponsors of UL until 1968. Sponsorship and membership was then broadened to include representatives of consumer interests, governmental bodies or agencies, education, public safety bodies, safety experts, standardization experts, and public utilities, in addition to the insurance industry.

UL has expanded its testing services to over 13,000 manufacturers throughout the world. Over one billion UL "labels" are used each year on products listed by Underwriters' Laboratories.

Underwriters' Laboratories, Inc. is chartered as a not-for-profit organization without capital stock under the laws of the state of Delaware, to establish, maintain, and operate laboratories for the examination and testing of devices, systems, and materials.

Its objectives, as stated in the Certificate of Incorporation are: "By scientific investigation, study, experiments and tests, to determine the relation of various materials, devices, products, equipment, constructions, methods, and systems to hazards appurtenant thereto or to the use thereof, affecting life and property, and to ascertain, define and publish standards, classifications and specifications for materials, devices, equipment, construction, methods, and systems affecting such hazards, and other information tending to reduce and prevent loss of life and property from such hazards."

The corporate headquarters, together with one of the testing laboratories, is located at 207 East Ohio St., Chicago, Illinois.

Underwriters' Laboratories, Inc. has a total staff of over 1,800 employees. More than 400 persons are engaged in engineering work, and of this number approximately 270 are graduate engineers. Supplementing the engineering staff are more than 500 factory inspectors.

Underwriters' Laboratories, Inc.'s engineering functions are divided between these six departments:

> Electrical
> Burglary Protection and Signaling
> Casualty and Chemical Standards
> Fire Protection
> Heating, Air-Conditioning, and Refrigeration
> **Marine**

Testing for Safety

A submittor desiring to secure an investigation and report on a product may write Underwriters' Laboratories, Inc. giving a brief description of the product. From this information, it is possible to classify and determine the nature and extent of the necessary examination and test. An application form is then sent to the submittor specifying in detail the limitations of the responsibility of Underwriters' Laboratories, Inc., the character and number of samples to be furnished, the cost limit, the work to be performed under the application, and the type and extent of inspection service to be established if and when the product is found acceptable.

At the completion of the investigation, a report is rendered to the submittor, indicating the findings. If the investigation disclosed any objectionable features, these must be corrected and revised samples found acceptable before Listing can be published. With some new products a report including the recommendations of the staff, may be submitted to one or more of the four Engineering Councils of Underwriters' Laboratories, Inc. These Councils are composed of prominent men who have outstanding knowledge and field experience in areas of public safety, and are designated as Fire, Automotive and Casualty, Electrical, and Burglary Protection Councils. Final action and Listing of an appliance or material may be dependent upon endorsement of the recommendation by the Council concerned. This provides a countercheck of the findings of the staff with the judgment of men of wide field experience.

A manufacturer whose product meets the Laboratories' requirements is provided with a Procedure prepared by the Laboratories' engineers as a part of the work under the application. This Procedure describes and illustrates the product in detail, particularly its construction and test performance. It becomes the manufacturer's guide for future production and is used by Laboratories' inspectors for periodic review of the Listed product. These Procedures are constantly kept up to date by co-operation with the manufacturer to cover changes in the product or additions to the line.

Of equal importance with examination and testwork is the follow-up program in the factory of clients and in the market place. The follow-up service is designed to serve as a formal check on the supervision which the manufacturer exercises to determine compliance of the product with the applicable requirements of the Laboratories.

The manufacturer must conduct specified examinations and tests to be certain the manufactured item is in compliance with the applicable UL requirements. The Laboratories' representatives make frequent visits to the factory in which the products are manufactured for the purpose of checking the efficiency of the manufacturer's own inspection program.

Should examination or test by the Laboratories' representative disclose features not in compliance with the requirements, the manufacturer is required to either correct such items or remove any UL identification from the product. In some cases, examination and tests are conducted by the Laboratories on products purchased on the open market which serve as a countercheck on factory inspection work.

Inspection centers and representatives are located in 189 cities in the United States and Puerto Rico, and in 29 foreign countries including Canada, Mexico, Japan, Israel, South Africa, and several in Western Europe.

More than 155,000 factory follow-up inspections are conducted on listed products each year by the UL inspection force.

Products Tested

Each year over 25,000 new products are tested for safety by "UL".

Products tested and listed by Underwriters' Laboratories are used by virtually every segment of our society. Electric tooth brushes and roofing materials, toasters and air conditioners, fire doors and gasoline pumps are just a few of the many thousands of items listed by the Laboratories.

Engineers, through vigorous testing procedures and careful examination of products, insure that potential hazards are evaluated and proper safeguards are provided.

The goals of all the Laboratories' testing is safety for the public—in the home, at school, in industry, and in business.

The Electrical Department is the largest of five engineering departments. Safety evaluations are made on hundreds of different types of appliances for use in the home, in commercial buildings, schools and in factories. The scope of the work in this department also includes electrical construction materials used within buildings to distribute electrical power from the meter location to the electrical outlet.

Fire Protection is UL's second largest safety-testing department. It utilizes many types and sizes of fire "furnaces" to test the fire resistance of floors, ceilings, walls, columns, and safes. Another "furnace" tests the burning characteristics of materials. Complete buildings have been specifically designed for testing sprinkler systems for high-rise warehouses. Testing the effectiveness of fire extinguishing equipment is an important function of this department. Many research projects are undertaken to determine causes and develop effective control over actual fire situations.

Work performed by this department includes field inspection of certificated premises, central stations, fire alarm signaling stations, as well as evaluation of devices and systems designed to prevent burglarious attack or to assist in detection or apprehension of burglars. Equipment related to fire detection and alarm devices is also tested and evaluated.

Products tested vary from the smallest units for home use to the larger commercial installations. Standards and procedures have been developed that recognize the testing requirements for customized equipment.

This department has facilities for analysis and chemical testing of materials and products such as cleaning liquids, flame resistant fabrics, and insulation for electrical wiring. Flammability tests are conducted on basic plastic materials.

231

Products tested for casualty hazards include: step ladders, floor coating materials, and pressure cookers. Automotive products are also tested by this group.

The newest addition to UL facilities is the Marine Department (formerly the Yacht Safety Bureau) in Westwood, New Jersey. Testing of pleasure boats and equipment is done at this location.

Underwriters' Laboratories, Inc. also publishes annually Lists of manufacturers whose products are listed. These Lists are kept up to date by Bi-Monthly Supplements. The seven Lists include:

Accidents, Automotive, and Burglary Protection Equipment
Building Materials
Fire Protection Equipment
Electrical Appliance and Utilization Equipment
Electrical Construction Materials
Hazardous Location Equipment
Gas and Oil Equipment

Underwriters' Laboratories, Inc. presently publishes more than 250 Standards for Safety for materials, devices, constructions, and methods, and makes copies available to interested parties. An Index of these Standards is available at no cost.

UL undertakes numerous research projects in areas of safety. Over 50 Research Bulletins have been published and are available. Write for Directory of Research Bulletins.

Several color, sound, 16mm motion pictures are available on a loan basis showing UL's work in testing for public safety.

Selected Bibliography

PUBLIC DOCUMENTS

Advisory Commission on Intergovernmental Relations. *Building Codes: A Program for Intergovernmental Reform.* 1966.

National Commission on Urban Problems. *Building the American City.* Report of the National Commission on Urban Problems to the Congress and to the President of the United States. 1968.

President's Committee on Urban Housing. *A Decent Home.* 1968.

Thompson, George N. *Preparation and Revision of Building Codes.* BMS 116. 1949.

Vice President's Handbook for Local Officials: A Guide to Federal Assistance for Local Governments. 1967.

BOOKS AND PAMPHLETS

Ancient Rome. Cited by R. C. Colling and Hal Colling. *Modern Building Inspection.* Los Angeles: Building Standards Monthly Publishing Company, 1950.

Barnard, Chester I. *The Functions of The Executive.* Cambridge: Harvard University Press, 1968.

Bartell, Joseph E. "Analysis of the BOCA Codes". *Local Building Regulations.* Edited by Paul E. Baseler. Chicago: Building Officials Conference of America, Inc., 1963.

Burnham, James. "Some Administrators Unkindly View Congress". *Public Administration: Readings in Institutions, Processes, Behavior.* Edited by Robert T. Golembiewski, Frank Gibson and Goeffry Y. Cornog. Chicago: Rand McNally and Company, 1965.

Chamber of Commerce of The United States. *Building Codes and Construction Progress.* Washington, D.C.: Chamber of Commerce of the United States, 1951.

Chamber of Commerce of The United States. *Building Codes for Community Development and Construction Progress.* Washington, D.C.: Chamber of Commerce of the United States, 1964.

Demarest, William. *Building Codes: Product Approvals.* New Haven: Ludlow-Bookman, 1964.

Downs, Anthony. *Inside Bureaucracy.* Boston: Little, Brown and Company, 1966.

Gardner, John W. *Excellence: Can We Be Equal and Excellent Too?* New York: Harper and Row, 1961.

Grodzins, Morton. "The Federal System". *The American Political System: Notes and Readings.* Edited by Bernard E. Brown and John C. Wahlke. Homewood. The Dorsey Press, 1967.

Merton, Robert K. "Bureaucratic Structure and Personality". *A Sociological Reader on Complex Organizations.* Edited by Amitai Etzioni. New York: Holt, Rinehart and Winston, Inc., 1969.

National Fire Protection Association. "Objects, Membership and Functions". *1968 Yearbook and Committee List.* Boston: National Fire Protection Association, 1968.

Parsons, Douglas E. *Building Codes and the Producers of Building Products.* Washington: The Producers Council, Inc., 1967.

Rhyne, Charles S. *Survey of The Law of Building Codes.* Washington: American Institute of Architects, National Association of Home Builders, 1960.

Simon, Herbert A., Donald W. Smithburg, and Victor A. Thompson. *Public Administration.* New York: Alfred A. Knopf, Inc., 1950.

Trull, Edna. *Administration of Regulatory Inspectional Services in American Cities.* New York: Municipal Administration Service, 1932.

Uicker, John J. "The Use of Standards in Building Codes". *Local Building Regulations.* Edited by Paul E. Baseler. Chicago: Building Officials Conference of America, 1963.

Waldo, Dwight. *The Study of Public Administration.* New York: Random House, 1955.

ARTICLES AND PERIODICALS

"Big Government—Is It Out of Hand?" *U. S. News and World Report,* March 24, 1969. pp. 28-30.

"The Code Problem and What to Do About It". *American Builder,* March, 1963.

Federal Register, December 10, 1965, cited in BOCA NEWS, XIV, (February 1966).

Howe, Harold II. "Changing the Pecking Order". *Civil Service Journal,* IX, July-September, 1968.

Polatsek, David F. " 'Who Goes There'—The Right of Entry and Housing Code Enforcement". *Journal of Urban Law,* Vol. XLVI, Issue 2, 1969.

Veysey, Arthur. "The Great London Fire". *Chicago Tribune Sunday Magazine*, March 5, 1967.

REPORTS

Brown, James R., Rita C. Griswold, and Dale M. Sharkey. *A Study Concerning the Need for Uniform Building Code for the Capitol Region.* Prepared for the Land Use and Housing Committee of the Regional Advisory Committee by the Regional Affairs Center, University of Hartford. Hartford: Regional Affairs Center, 1967.

Index

A

Administrative Law, 107; inducement methods, 107; monopoly of attorneys, 107; public relations, 107; rules of, 107

Administrative relief, 142

Advisory Commission on Intergovernmental Relations, 58

Air pollution control, 101

American Academy of Code Administration, 188

American Insurance Association, 7, 38

American Society for Testing and Materials, 21

American Society of Heating, Refrigeration and Air Conditioning Engineers, 38

American Society of Mechanical Engineers, 38

Appeals, 70, 172

Authoritative Agencies, 32

B

Building Codes,
  Authority for, 51
  Cities, use in major, 9
  Criticism of, 52
  Federal, is it necessary, 51
    analysis of recommendations, 65; bureaucratic incest, 57; federally encouraged non-uniformity, 40; independent power of the bureaucracy, 57; recommendation of Advisory Commission on Intergovernmental Relations, 58; of National Commission on Urban Problems, 62; President's Committee on Urban Housing, 56; summary of recommendations, 64; what is needed, 57; who wants it, 56

Fire limits, 16; object of, 16; provisions for, 16

Fire safety, 16; emphasis on, 16

Historical development, 5

Local codes, 46; big hurdle, 46; excessive construction costs due to, 45; need for maximum requirements, 46; problems for mass producers, 46

Model codes, 37;
    Basic, 9; geographical usage, 9; published by, 9; scope of, 9
    National, 7; first model, 7; published by, 7; insurance interests, 8; major emphasis, 8
    Southern Standard, 9; geographical usage, 9; published by, 9; scope of, 9
    Uniform, 9; geographical usage, 9; published by, 9; scope of, 9

Philosophy of, 13

Requirement in, 13; basis for, 13; construction, types of, 17; environmental, 19; exits, theory of, 18; fire safety, 16, 18; height and area limitations, 16; influences on, 31; occupancy or use group classification, 17; offsetting use hazards, 17; safety to life, 18; structural, 19

Scope of, 14

Types of, 15; performance, 15; specification, 15

State, 10; forms of, 10

What they are, 13

Building department, 102; is a law enforcement agency, 102; its status, 111; its clientele group, 112, 115